PAUL EHRLICH

PAUL EHRLICH

By

MARTHA MARQUARDT

With an Introduction by
SIR HENRY DALE

Henry Schuman · New York

TO THE MEMORY
OF
PAUL EHRLICH

PREFACE

THIS book is an extension of my previous work, 'Paul Ehrlich als Mensch und Arbeiter', which was published in memory of him on the seventieth anniversary of his birth, 14 March, 1924, by Deutsche Verlagsgesellschaft, Stuttgart. Only a few copies of that work now remain, a considerable part of the edition having been destroyed during the Nazi regime in Germany. I limited my first book to personal reminiscences of this great man gathered during the thirteen years, up to his death in 1915, during which I had been happy and privileged to work for him. I have taken from it for this new book what seemed to me appropriate.

My interest in Ehrlich's remarkable life has deepened throughout the years. Little details have come to me from his family. I have learnt fresh items here and there, from his friends, and from remarks made by Ehrlich himself which return to my memory or which I have found in his written notes. I have also found passages of special importance in his published papers. All these things have combined to form a living image of this great personality. They make a rounded picture which, though not pretending to be a full biography, contains so many intimate details that I hope it will interest the reader. It will allow him to follow closely the different stages in the life of this great genius, and show how Ehrlich worked, struggled and finally arrived at the invention of 606 which made him famous throughout the world.

The greater part of the present work was finished in 1940 but remained unpublished owing to the exigencies of the war. In December 1946 I was able to revisit Frankfurt for a few weeks, and found a number of Ehrlich's old staff still at their posts in the Institutes in the Paul Ehrlich-Strasse. I was deeply touched to see their delight at being able to talk about old times and their unforgotten, unforgettable chief. It pleased them all to help me look round in every corner of the partly bomb-destroyed Institutes and collect publications of Ehrlich's which I needed, and little objects he had used which are of historical interest.

v

Ehrlich's whole life was one long fight for the promotion of medical science in the service of mankind. He had a deep-rooted, unwavering optimism, aiming always at perfection and ever more difficult targets, supported always by an unshakable faith in progress. He could have done much more for humanity had not his life been cut short by his premature death at the age of sixty-one. Striving for the health and happiness of the world he had overtaxed his own physical strength, and burnt the candle at both ends. Of him it may truly be said:

> Was vergangen kehrt nicht wieder,
> Aber ging es leuchtend nieder,
> Leuchtet's lange noch zurück.

> (What has passed will ne'er return,
> But if it sank in dazzling flame,
> Flashes of light will still remain.)

ACKNOWLEDGMENTS

To the late Sir Almroth Wright, M.D., F.R.S., Professor of Pathology, Director of the Inoculation Department, St. Mary's Hospital, London, who was for more than fifty years a friend of Ehrlich, I am deeply indebted for having made it possible for me to come to London three years ago and there finish my work on Ehrlich. I owe to him and also to Sir Henry Dale, O.M., F.R.S., Chairman of the Wellcome Trust, likewise a friend of Ehrlich's of long standing, my heartfelt thanks for all the encouragement and help necessary for such a difficult task, and to them I am extremely grateful. I am also most grateful to Miss Johnston Abraham for revising my English, and to my publishers for their constant consideration.

MARTHA MARQUARDT

London, 1949.

CONTENTS

INTRODUCTION

PAUL EHRLICH died in 1915, the second year of the First World War. It may seem strange that we have not yet had a full and well-documented biography of a man whose work and ideas have meant so much for medical science, and through medical science for mankind. For I do not think that it can be doubted, that Ehrlich's way of thinking, and the lines of research which he opened to exploration, have provided a central impulse for that rapid, even revolutionary change, in the whole aspect of the preventive and curative treatment of infections, which stands out as one of the great achievements of the half century now ending, even in an age of such general advance in science.

Many in the world at large, through the film which was made about him and in other ways, have probably come to think of Ehrlich as the man who discovered Salvarsan (606), and thus gave to the world the first specific and radically effective cure for syphilis. Not so many, I believe, are aware that, nearly twenty years earlier, the possibility of making practical use, as remedies, of the substances, antitoxins, etc., formed by the body's natural reactions of immunity, was made effective by Ehrlich's masterly researches at that time. The major credit for that achievement, as not seldom happens, had been given to others, such as von Behring, who had made the primary and relatively easy observation that such natural antidotes are formed. It was Ehrlich, however, who showed how their production could be so stimulated that they could be obtained in sufficient strength for practical use in treatment; and it was he who devised accurate methods for measuring their curative potencies in terms of permanent standards, and defined units of activity in which these values could be expressed—in which, in fact, they are still expressed, all over the world. And, in doing this, Ehrlich had further established, once and for all, the scientific principles which are fundamental to the measurement and dosage of a large class of modern remedies. And therewith, almost as a by-product of the direction of his thoughts and his interest towards the solution of such practical problems, Ehrlich's imaginative genius offered a startling theory of the nature of the reaction, by which the body of the patient makes itself immune from a further similar infection, by producing substances which fit with a perfect precision, and thus selectively combine with and neutralise, the particular agent or poison which they have to counteract. This 'side-chain' theory of Ehrlich rapidly permeated and gave shape and direction to the researches in this field of workers in all countries; and it has continued to be a principal factor in the rapid expansion of knowledge of the phenomena of immunity, allergy and related conditions. There were critics, of course, to whom Ehrlich made effective reply, not without a certain gusto; and I think that it is true that many, even of those who were glad to use Ehrlich's conceptions for their suggestive stimulus, were apt to regard them as an ingenious and convenient scaffolding for thought, and for the design of further experiments, rather than as a permanent addition to the structure of knowledge. Looking back from the present position, however, we may well be astonished to discover how well they have worn. It is of particular interest, indeed, to see what men who have worked on the subject in these recent years, long since Ehrlich died, and who have been able to use a wealth of chemical knowledge new since his time, are now making of these reactions, by which the body produces the specific antidotes of immunity. Investigators like the late Karl Landsteiner and, more recently, Linus Pauling appear, in fact, to be reaching conclusions about these phenomena which, though stated in modern terms, bear an ever closer resemblance to the conceptions which Ehrlich's brilliant and prophetic imagination was already generating some fifty years ago. Even the discovery of Salvarsan may be regarded as only the first major success, though the last one in Ehrlich's own lifetime, in a new kind of scientific quest which he had already begun some twenty years earlier. This was the search for substances which, by virtue of their chemical structure and combining properties, would directly attach themselves to, and be able thus to kill or weaken, the infecting organisms, but would leave the tissues of the infected patient unharmed. As early as 1891, with such an end in view, he had been testing the possibilities of methylene blue, a well-known dye, as a remedy for malaria; and he had been diverted for a time from that line of experiment, partly by the difficulty of using malaria infections, which were then available for such trials only in Man, and partly by the official request to him to bring order and accuracy into the use of the antitoxins. Ehrlich himself would hardly have regarded this latter as a diversion, however, since he recognised at once that these natural antidotes had, in far greater perfection than could ever be expected from the best artificial products of chemical synthesis, the very properties which he sought; by virtue of their selective combining properties they were the completely specific antagonists of the infecting organisms and their poisons, with no affinity for, and no effect upon, the body of the infected subject. Here, as Miss Marquardt shows so clearly in her biographical sketch, Ehrlich had come upon his ideal remedies, his 'magic bullets'.

It was not long, however, before he recognised that the use in practical medicine of these substances, formed by the natural reactions of immunity, had some drawbacks and limitations. The logical development of such methods, as we can see more clearly now, lies rather towards the production, wherever possible, of a permanent immunity in the subject himself by protective inoculation, than towards the further improvement of ready-made antitoxins and the like, for administration after infection has produced the disease. And, in any case, it was already clear to Ehrlich that there was a wide range of infections to which none of these methods of 'immunotherapy' offered any hope of successful application. By 1902, therefore, he was ready to return to his first trail, having now at his disposal, as experimental material, infections by trypanosomes (African sleeping-sickness, etc.) and later by spirochaetes (syphilis, relapsing fever, etc.), transmissible in the laboratory to mice, rats, rabbits and birds in any required numbers. Thus armed, he resumed the search for artificial remedies, with such chemical structures that they would exhibit the widest possible contrast between strong affinity for, and harmful action on, the infecting parasites, and lack or weakness of any such action on the tissues of the infected subject. Ehrlich threw himself now with full vigour into this new quest, which he termed 'Chemotherapy', to distinguish it from the pharmacology of those days, which, he maintained, had devoted itself to analysing the effects of drugs on the patient and his symptoms, but gave no information or help towards the discovery of better remedies to deal directly with the infective cause of his disease. And this new campaign, after minor and less permanent successes, was to culminate for Ehrlich himself with the finding of Salvarsan, and its establishment as a remedy of a new order of efficiency, in its power of dealing directly and radically with one of civilisation's most terrible scourges. For Miss Marquardt, whose book deals with Ehrlich's life and work as she knew them, with the intimate knowledge of a trusted secretary, the story naturally ends there.

But, though Salvarsan was thus to be the last of Ehrlich's direct and personal achievements in research, and certainly one of the greatest, it by no means represented the end, or the climax, of what his researches and his ideas were to do for science and for mankind. New remedies for sleeping sickness, for malaria and for other diseases due to protozoa, far better than any of which Ehrlich himself had knowledge, have been found since he died, by following the lead which he had given and the principles which he had laid down; and the same methods of chemotherapy have now also been extended, and with success beyond all expectation, to the specific treatment of the infections, commoner in our temperate zone, which are caused by bacteria. In Ehrlich's own time, and for twenty years after his death, the attempts to find an effective chemotherapy for these had yielded so little success, or promise of it, that it had almost come to be assumed that the method was, for some reason not known, unsuited to their treatment. Then, in 1935, Domagk's discovery of the action of 'Prontosil' opened the way to the series of the Sulphanilamide derivatives; and the revolutionary improvements which these effected, in the treatment of a number of common infections, played its part in the decision of Florey and his team to examine anew the chemotherapeutic possibilities of the half-forgotten Penicillin, which Fleming had found ten years before. And the new enterprise inspired by the marvellous success of Penicillin has now led to the discovery of Streptomycin, and others are already in sight. But the central idea of experimental chemotherapy, and the initial impulse to its present triumphant march forward, came from Paul Ehrlich; and, as Miss Marquardt so clearly shows, the germ of it is already to be discerned in his earliest publication, before he had even completed his graduation in medicine.

How has it come about, then, that we have not yet had a full biography of a man, whose life and activities still mean so much for the present and the future health of mankind? I think that there are several reasons. The first, and the most obvious, is that it would have been natural to look for the author of such an account among the distinguished German workers in the field of the medical sciences, who were Ehrlich's own close friends and associates. Even if any of these had had a special gift for biography, however, by the time that the writing might, in the normal course, have been undertaken, they had been driven far and wide across the world by the Hitler revolution. When it became safe to mention Ehrlich's name again, in the country which he had loved and served with such devotion, the Second World War had come and gone, and the possibility of a life of Ehrlich from his own Germany had again receded to an unknown future.

Then I am disposed to think that an attempt to write Ehrlich's biography at full length, with copious citation of his voluminous correspondence, his scientific publications and other relevant documents, would encounter peculiar difficulties. For there can seldom, if ever, have been a life more completely absorbed than Ehrlich's was, in advanced scientific activities and ideas, the details of which it would be very difficult to make interesting, or even intelligible, beyond the circle of a relatively small number of experts. I am sure that there are many who can confirm Miss Marquardt's memory and my own experience, that, although Ehrlich had his occasional intervals of relaxation, in which he could show an almost childlike enjoyment of quiet fun and simple pleasures, his normal waking hours were filled with an extraordinary concentration of interest on his own scientific ideas and plans for research. A visitor to Ehrlich would find himself, after the briefest of formal welcomes, swept into a torrent of excited exposition of Ehrlich's latest findings and theories, copiously illustrated with blue-pencil diagrams on any handy surface; and, even if his own work and interests lay in a not distant field of medical research, the visitor was likely to find himself quite early out of his depth and to resign himself to submersion. When I myself had my first interview with Ehrlich, I was introduced to him by a German friend who wished to take the opportunity of discussing aspects of his own work in which

B

he hoped to interest Ehrlich. When we emerged from the encounter I confessed rather meekly that, probably through slowness in following Ehrlich's tumultuous German, I had not understood much of the enthusiastic monologue; and my friend astonished me by replying, 'Ich auch nicht'—'Neither did I'.

Anybody, it seems to me, who attempted a complete and systematic biography of such a man, doing full justice to the main activities and interests of his life, would find it very difficult not to overweight the account with material fit only for specialists; and the light relief, the sections dealing with the subject's personal relations and characteristics, with his habits and tastes and with the general manner of his approach to his life's work, might too easily, by contrast, take on the aspect of caricature.

Altogether, then, it seems probable that the best solution of the problem is to be found by dividing it. We should have, then, on the one hand, an account of Ehrlich's scientific work and its significance, written by specialists for a relatively small circle of experts. And we should have, on the other hand, an intimately personal account of the man, of the way in which he worked and planned, and of his joys, his triumphs and his frustrations, written by somebody who was closely associated with him in his personal and his working life, who could record impressions received without previous specialist knowledge, and who could look at his fads and his foibles with eyes of indulgent affection, not blind to faults of temper or freaks of vanity, but seeing all with kindly humour, as features of a complex character. And I believe, indeed, that we now have accounts of both kinds, dealing with Ehrlich and his work.

The account by specialists of his scientific achievements and their significance, as seen in the year before he died, was written by the devotion of a number of the men who had worked as his assistants and his colleagues, as a present for his sixtieth birthday in 1914.[1] Each of them took an appropriate aspect of his work and provided a full chapter on it, discussing in detail what Ehrlich and his co-workers had achieved in that direction. The articles naturally varied in style, and in the degree to which Ehrlich's personal idiosyncrasies and the special quality of his

---

[1] Paul Ehrlich, *Eine Darstellung seines wissenschaftlichen Wirkens*, 14 March, 1914 (Gustav Fischer, Jena).

vision were to be discerned through the fabric of highly technical details. The book has a great and permanent value, however; I can only think, indeed, of one possibly desirable addition to our sources of information about Ehrlich and his work, at that level of specialised knowledge; and that is a complete assembly, in one edition, of all his not very voluminous publications. Perhaps we may have it some day.

On the other hand, we have presented to us here, in Miss Marquardt's book, what I judge to be as good a description, as sympathetic, as lively and as accurately appreciative as anybody is likely to be able to give us, of Paul Ehrlich as a man, and of the factors of heredity, education and experience that went to the making of a character and a personality so full of unexpected contrasts and fascinating conundrums. She has collected with a courageous industry all that she could find to add detail to her picture, in spite of all the difficulties and dangers created by the Nazi revolution, her own voluntary exile, the Second World War which found her in occupied Paris, and the devastation which it left in Frankfurt. She has not given us a formally planned biography; one has the feeling that she has striven to give her account a chronological order, but has been unable to resist the lure of anecdotes and digressions, whenever these appeared to give more life to the portrait, by showing up some features of kindliness, enthusiasm, remoteness, humour, or petulance, in the man she admired and served with such complete devotion. My own knowledge of Ehrlich was comparatively fragmentary, though it went back almost to the days, more than forty-five years ago, when Miss Marquardt first began to be his secretary. I saw enough of him, however, then and later, to feel certain that Miss Marquardt has given us a vital and an essentially authentic picture of him. I can imagine that many readers, who did not know Ehrlich, may suspect her of exaggeration, finding it difficult to believe that anybody could live and do great work at such a pitch of excitement and explosive emotions, or sprinkle his speech with such a rattle of parenthetic inquiries, or depend almost entirely on strong cigars and mineral water for his sustenance. I can only say that, while appearances must, I suppose, have been deceptive in some directions, Ehrlich did, in fact, look just like that to me also. The portrait is for me a very faithful as well as a vivid one. When Miss Marquardt allowed me to read her manuscript, I did wonder, indeed, whether she might not, with advantage, have omitted certain items— whether some of the detailed accounts of Ehrlich's resentments and grievances, or of his anger, on occasion, with colleagues who were not just tamely obedient, ought not to be removed, or subdued, in the interest of a true impression of his greatness. Miss Marquardt, however, was sure that records of any actual and significant happenings could only help to complete the picture of the real Ehrlich; she felt sure that his resentment and his anger were justified and, in any case, were as essential to the truth of the portrait as were his more amiable and endearing reactions. I do not doubt that she was right, and that she ought to give us everything characteristic of Ehrlich that her recollection can preserve, sunlit, as it is, with a humorous tenderness. And so she has woven thorns as well as flowers into the wreath of her memories, and yet it seems to me to be a very fragrant garland that she has fashioned. I hope that many will fall under the spell of its enchantment, and that it will help a new circle of admirers, far wider than that of the followers of medicine or other sciences, to place the fame of Paul Ehrlich, as a wonderful human being as well as a great discoverer, upon the pinnacle which it ought to occupy in the regard of a grateful world.

H. H. D.

CHAPTER I

CHILDHOOD AND SCHOOLDAYS

The Child is Father of the Man.—WORDSWORTH.

THE face is the mirror of the soul. The house where we were born, our parents, family and surroundings, all make impressions which sink deep into our hearts and later on affect our characters and actions. It is especially interesting to learn some-

Strehlen (Upper Silesia)

thing of the childhood of a famous man; to see how his career started, and how his character developed.

Paul Ehrlich was born on a beautiful day in early March in the year 1854, a day when refreshing breezes laden with the fragrance of newly ploughed soil gave a foretaste of Spring and warmth and sun. Even in the rough climate of Eastern Germany Nature was awakening. Snowdrops pushed their heads through the winter cover of the earth and anemones appeared in the woods in innumerable thousands, spreading a lovely white carpet over the dark layers of decayed winter leaves. His parents longed for a son, for so far only daughters had been born to

I

them; and on 14 March, 1854, their wish was granted, and Paul, their beloved only son, was born.

The child of a prosperous Jewish family, citizens of Strehlen in Upper Silesia, Paul Ehrlich was brought up in the traditions of his people and developed sound principles and a strong personality. His grandfather and his parents are said to have been remarkable people in their time; and it is said, too, that his grandfather, with his beautifully shaped head framed by snow-white ringlets and his intelligent eyes full of life, resembled

Ehrlich's Grandfather

Alexander von Humboldt, the famous naturalist and scientific writer. His grandfather was deeply interested in the history of Strehlen, in the outskirts of which the Huguenots had been allowed by Frederick the Great to settle in the eighteenth century. He was also very much interested in natural science. Even at the age of eighty he gave popular scientific lectures.

Paul Ehrlich's father, who was an inn-keeper, is described as a man of keen judgment, with a cheerful manner and full of good humour. But in spite of these lively characteristics he would sometimes sit at the window for hours talking to himself, accompanying his words with movements of the head and gesticulations of the hand. When speaking to others he would pour out his words and sentences in a strange hurry, introduce a jest, repeating it several times loudly in the conversation, and laughing over it. He had a special liking for snuff and used his snuff-box a great deal. He was the kind of man about whom one would say: 'he always has his head in the clouds', and he took no great interest in everyday business affairs. For this reason Paul's mother had to be all the more far-sighted, skilful and zealous. She was the real heart and soul of

Ehrlich's Father

the family, and not only took wonderful care of the large household but also attended personally to the customers of their inn, which was called the 'Krug zum Rautenkranz' ('The Tavern of the Wreath of Rue'). She was highly esteemed by all the guests staying in the house on account of her cheerful manner and sterling character. Always kindly towards the employees, she could also, if necessary, maintain her authority with sternness and energy.

The boy Paul obviously inherited many of his characteristics from his parents and his grandfather. He resembled the latter in appearance and in his liking

Ehrlich's Mother

for natural science; perhaps also his gift for chemistry came from his grandfather. He inherited from his father the hasty manner of speech, accompanied by gesticulations, and punctuated by the frequent interjections which later in his life became almost proverbial, such as 'Wissen Sie, verstehen Sie . . .' (you

Ehrlich's Birthplace

know, you understand), . . . 'Ja, natürlich, natürlich . . .' (Yes, certainly, certainly . . .) 'Ja, wieso denn, wieso denn? . . .' (Yes, but how so, how so?) . . . 'Wundervoll' . . . 'Grossartig!' . . . (Wonderful . . . marvellous!) . . . *'re vera'* . . . *'eo ipso'* . . . or, when he was indignant with someone: 'Fauler Kopf' (lazy head) . . . *'caput pigerrimum'* or . . . 'Ungeschickter Taperkerl,' an invention of his own, meaning an unskilled or awkward person, a clumsy good-for-nothing.

These interjections were characteristic and showed unmistakably Ehrlich's spirit. To mention only some of them, 'Wieso denn . . . wieso denn?' or 'Ja, wieso denn . . . wieso denn?' showed impatience, pushing onward, nervousness, and expressed astonishment: while the drawn out 'A-l-s-o' came hesitatingly, holding back, reflecting, and he used to say: 'A-l-s-o, was hatten wir gesagt?' (what was it that we said?), and 'A-l-s-o, jetzt wollen wir mal schreiben' (now we shall write). His friendly 'Tag ook' in which the 'g', according to the Silesian

Sitting-Room

idiom, was pronounced very hard, had quite another meaning than one would think it had. It was not merely 'good morning' or 'good day', but it was like a welcoming greeting saying 'how nice that you have come', 'pleased to see you', and he had this kind 'Tag ook' for everybody who came in to see him.

His friends used to say he could not speak or write a single sentence which did not contain at least one of these ejaculations or, because of his fondness for Latin, a Latin expression. He used, as we shall see later in the course of his career, vivid forms of expression for all scientific conceptions. All his ideas took on with him a visual character, and his visualized descriptions, to explain scientific phenomena as he really saw them, not infrequently produced in scientifically unimaginative people an ironical smile or shake of the head. On one occasion he was even called by the mocking name of 'Doctor Fantasy'. His unusual habit of smoking very strong cigars while still only a young hospital-assistant seems to have been an inheritance from his father, while on the other hand his conscientiousness in working,

Karl Weigert

his talent for organisation, his noble mind and kind-heartedness, evidently came from his mother.

There is not much to be said about Paul at school in his native town of Strehlen, except that he showed the beginnings of great talent, and that already at the age of eight he used to have the chemist of his little town make cough-drops for him after his own prescription. When at school in Breslau he liked to try chemical experiments, and during the holidays made all sorts of mixtures in the laundry at home. His cousin Karl Weigert, who was nine years older and already showed promise of his later eminence in pathology, was looked upon by the young Ehrlich as a model, and profoundly influenced his further development. These two were great friends all their lives.

After having left the Strehlen school and gone to Breslau College he got on exceedingly well in Latin, and was seen to be very gifted in mathematics. Nevertheless, he longed for the holidays, and when they came all his books were thrown in a corner and his mind was occupied with entirely different things.

Paul had hardly arrived home—so we are told by a companion of his youth, a playfellow aged only seven at that time— when he was surrounded by all the schoolboys of Strehlen from seven to sixteen as soon as they learned that he was back; and with this swarm of enthusiastic followers he would spend all his holidays. They were together, here, there and everywhere, getting into mischief as boys always will. They went out to catch all sorts of animals, salamanders, lizards, frogs and mice. They played brigands in the stony hills and pits around Strehlen, and in these games Paul always had to take command and lead them. It is reported that on one occasion he received a sound thrashing from the others. This is not surprising, if we consider that it was meant as a sort of reprisal by the physically stronger boys against their spiritual leader: as a little revenge, so to speak, for his superior intellect which did not in the least diminish the real love of his followers.

Ehrlich's whole life was a struggle and a fight. He would not submit to being wronged, was always ready to defend himself and, if necessary, to attack. This militant characteristic of his was appropriate to his time. The fate of his Silesian homeland had never been easy. In the thirteenth century there had been invasions and attacks by the Mongols from the East, and in the fifteenth century there were the wars of the Hussites which followed the martyrdom of Johann Hus in 1415. In the eighteenth century came the separation of Silesia from Austria by annexation during the three Silesian wars of Frederick the Great and the Seven Years' War which followed. These two epochs lasted almost twenty years, during which the country was never at peace. Early in the nineteenth century Napoleon's troops on their way to Russia flooded the country. From the suppressed German Revolution of 1848, though it raged particularly in Western and South-western Germany, some waves had inevitably been carried far into the Eastern part of the country. During this period Paul Ehrlich was born. Then followed the wars of 1864–66 and 1871, and all these events must have had a deep influence on the growing boy.

Ehrlich referred to himself as 'timid', which was not a true description. But in the depths of his soul he had an inexhaustible source of tenderness and kindness, and upon this everyone could rely absolutely. His compassion for the sufferings of others was so strong that he would almost feel them as his own. Once, only once, during all the years I worked for him, I was suddenly ill and asked to go home. Ehrlich saw that I was in pain: he said nothing, just nodded, but his features took on an expression of deep affliction as though he were suffering himself.

There are many stories of Paul's exploits during the school holidays. One morning the servant girl at his home, going into the wash-house to light the fire, was startled on opening the door and ran back into the house with screams of terror. Hardly able to speak in her agitation she made it clear to Paul's mother that something awful was going on in the wash-house. Together they hurried down, the mother leading the way, and saw that all sorts of little animals, lizards, frogs, salamanders and others were crawling and creeping about. The whole laundry was alive with them. Evidently the boys had brought in these creatures on the evening before, put them into water in the wash-tubs and stowed them away in safety, each kind separate from another; but they had all escaped during the night and made a real Witches' Sabbath together.

Paul was coming in when this was discovered, and his mother caught him by the ear; but he protested, taking from his pockets and cap insects and worms and other living things which he had just caught, saying that his 'animals' must be fed. To his intense disappointment he received stern instructions from his mother to take 'that crazy stuff' to the nearest pond immediately and leave it there; and he had, ruefully, to obey. It is probable that his mother, with a smile lurking at the corner of her mouth, added that he would have been better employed in taking more care over his holiday-tasks to which he never paid much attention; and no doubt her eyes were thoughtful as she looked after him and wondered what might become of her boy when he grew up.

Paul's former playmate also tells how he once came home on holiday with one of his trunks full of opera-hats. And in each of his coat pockets was found a clothes' brush which he had absent-mindedly borrowed from friends he had visited. He never packed his bags and trunks properly, but, when holiday time came, would seize them as they were, without looking to see what was in them, and hurry off. The holidays were always wonderful, his friend reports, for in addition to their other games Paul also organized open-air dancing and amateur theatricals for the boys and their sisters.

Young Paul aged sixteen

When he had to go back to Breslau and school, young Paul always found himself faced with disagreeable duties. Of course, he had not done any of his holiday-tasks—had not even looked at them. He lodged in the house of his form-master, Dr. Munck, and in his small barely furnished room he would unpack his baggage. His dear mother had put many good things into it: in the first place a big sausage, which he liked very much. This treasure was put on the table, and next to it his books and note-books. Still feeling in cheerful holiday mood, but already looking with distaste at his books, he would kick at his bags on the floor and then sit down at the table to begin his studies; for the next day was the beginning of term.

The tasks in Latin were always done quickly, without a pause, and while writing them he would repeat the Latin sentences aloud. Latin was his hobby, and all his life he liked to use it both in speaking and writing. He loved it on account of its logical structure. Difficult mathematical problems were also easily solved. He was sure of himself and did not need to spoil his holiday with home-work in these subjects. But when it came to the German Composition it was a different matter—he was at a standstill. He would bite his penholder, scratch behind his

ear, run all five fingers through his blond tuft of hair, and
finally rub it down with the palm of his hand until it was entirely flat. This was a habit which remained characteristic of
Ehrlich, especially in his later years, when he wanted to explain
one of his complicated theories to some of his friends or colleagues. It did not help very much, however, with the German
Composition. Now and then he would take a bite of the good
sausage his mother had given him, and when at last the composition was finished he found that the sausage was finished as
well. At the end of his strenuous work—both writing and eating
—he had to hold his cheek and rub it sadly. He had toothache.

When the examinations were approaching, Paul had to study
hard, even at night, with a primitive kerosene lamp and a
meagre fire in the little stove in his room. Often, as well as preparing for his examinations, he had to write a letter to his
parents and also a German Composition. He did not at all like
doing either of these. Late one evening when Dr. Munck went
up to see what he was doing, he found him looking blankly at his
note-paper and biting his pen.

'Hullo, Paul, is it *so* hard to write a letter home?' he asked.

Paul made a grimace.

'Just write about what you've been doing,' the master said
with a smile, and on leaving the room he warned the boy:
'Don't stay up too late!'

But the next morning Dr. Munck came into Paul's room to
look for him, because all the other boys had already left for
school. He found on the bed what seemed to be a big bundle.
Coming nearer and lifting a corner of the bundle he found a
quilted cover, a dressing-gown, a jacket, then another jacket, all
on top of each other, and then, at last, a head. The head be-
longed to Paul, who, thus muffled up, had fallen asleep and
failed to wake at the proper time. When he did wake it was too
late to go to school that morning. But Dr. Munck asked:

'Have you done the composition?'

Paul shook his head. 'N . . . o.'

'What are you going to do about it?'

'I shall tell the Headmaster.'

Dr. Munck had great difficulty in remaining serious, but
said:

'All right, then tell him.'

The next morning at school Paul said:

'I have not finished the German composition, Sir, but I shall deliver it in two weeks.'

'All right, Ehrlich,' the master replied with a little twitch at the corners of his mouth. But the composition was *never* delivered . . . the Headmaster knew it would not be.

At length the time came for Paul to take his school-leaving examination. This consisted of written papers and oral tests. He hated examinations of any kind, and all his life he profoundly pitied everybody who had to pass one. The written papers came first. The Latin was done extremely well, and his achievements in all branches of natural science were so good that Paul could have been excused from the *viva voce* examination. But his German Composition, sad to say, was definitely not so good.

The candidates for this final examination were all assembled in one room and had to write their German Composition under supervision. The subject, 'Life—a Dream', was written on the blackboard. Paul pondered, pulled the tip of his ear, bit his penholder, continued to brood, rubbed his tuft of hair and meditated deeply, his elbow on the table and his head on his hand.

The teacher, trying to rouse him, said good-naturedly:

'There, Paul, it is not as difficult as all that, is it?'

The boy made a rueful face. Then after a while he raised his head, and, still deep in thought, began to write, finishing his paper within the allotted time. He was the last of all the candidates to hand in his composition. The teacher smiled.

At first everything went well in the oral examinations which followed. His Latin was excellent as always, and in all other subjects he satisfied his examiners. But then came the German. The teachers stood together, doubt in their faces. The Headmaster held in his hand Paul's German Composition, on the margin of which a lot of remarks were written. He looked over the pages once more and then said sternly:

'Now, Ehrlich, will you please give us an explanation of what you have written! What does this mean?'

Paul, distressed and confused, began to stammer. 'Yes, well . . . then . . . thus, in this way . . . wissen Sie, verstehen Sie . . . (you know, you understand) . . . life *is* . . . *re vera* . . . *a chemical incident . . . a normal oxidation . . .* and the dream . . . the dream *also . . .* the dream is . . . the dream is a *fluorescence of the brain,*' he finished quickly.

The teachers were almost wringing their hands. The Headmaster whispered something. They all looked excited. He pointed several times emphatically to some of the passages in the composition. They shrugged their shoulders, and Paul stood before them like a poor sinner at the gates of heaven.

At last the Headmaster said to him:

'Ehrlich, you have done fine work in Latin, and also in other subjects, but your German Composition', and he shook his head with these words, 'your German Composition is wretchedly bad! For the honour of the college you should have done better than that! But on the strength of your good Latin and your other schoolwork we are inclined to recognise your examination as just satisfactory, and to pass you.'

The other teachers made a movement signifying that they agreed. Paul stood there with a hot blushing face. He bowed to the teachers confusedly and left the room. Then he ran at once to the Post Office and sent a telegram to his parents saying: 'Examination passed'. All his books flew into the corners of his room, he seized his bags, and home he went.

CHAPTER II

AT THE UNIVERSITY

FROM the very beginning young Paul found the Breslau University disappointing. He did not find things as interesting and scientific as he expected, and in many ways he did not know on what work to begin. He was interested only in biology, in which he was exceptionally well grounded, in organic chemistry with its constitutional formulae, and in histology—the microscopical study of the tissues. During the first term of University life he moved and went on to the newly founded University of Strassburg.

At this time, in the middle of the eighteen-seventies, the chemical works making aniline dyes in Germany frequently found new preparations which could be used in biological analysis. These interested the young student immensely. He undertook on his own initiative some histological staining experiments, and was so enthralled by this work of his own that he forgot and neglected all the regular university courses and studies.

His tutor at the University of Strassburg, Professor Waldeyer, had been the first German Professor to introduce the chemical outlook into medicine at a time when chemistry had not yet been admitted as an independent branch of science at German Universities but had to be studied as a Ph.D. course. He fully understood young Ehrlich's peculiarities and let him go his own way. He had expressed to all his students the desire that those who took part in his courses should continue to work after the lectures were over if they wished, and Paul gladly and frequently availed himself of this opportunity. On one of these occasions Professor Waldeyer found him late in the afternoon still at work in the laboratory busily engaged on some experiment. On coming nearer he found that the big laboratory table was looking terrible, being covered with spots of every possible colour. With an indulgent smile Professor Waldeyer asked:

'What are you up to now?'

Ehrlich had not interrupted his experiment when his tutor entered the laboratory. He now looked up, and handing his test tube to Professor Waldeyer he answered:

'I am experimenting with dyes, Sir.'

His fingers were covered with stains, and even his face showed traces of the dyes.

Professor Waldeyer held the test tube against the light and looked at some of the stained preparations which Ehrlich showed him. He convinced himself that the young student was not merely working according to the usual laboratory methods but was also experimenting on original lines, and with fine results. So he only said kindly, nodding his head:

'Well then, go on trying.'

In these experiments Ehrlich discovered a new variety of cell which he called 'Mast-cells'. He could show by his staining experiments exactly how the outlines of these cells were defined, and how the granules within them could be selectively stained. These promising experiments led him on to his extensive analytical studies of the staining process.

In later years Professor Waldeyer said that as a student Ehrlich seemed shy and very young, but with engaging manners and a great interest in scientific work. Even then the Professor was impressed by his personality and thought that he would have an important and distinguished career.

In his third term at the University, having passed his Physikum,[1] Ehrlich returned to the University of Breslau where he continued his studies in pathology and anatomy. This was evidently on the advice of his cousin Karl Weigert, and Ehrlich says in autobiographical notes which I have just found, that there—in Breslau—he had the opportunity 'to work in the laboratories of such prominent teachers as Professor Cohnheim and Professor Heidenhain'. He also says in these notes, that for his 'Physikum' he had to 'cram' into his head the necessary knowledge of chemistry and as a result became at once so much interested in it that he received the mark 'excellent' in this examination, despite the fact that the examiner, Professor Adolf von Beyer, did not know him at all.

'Adolf von Beyer also told my teacher Waldeyer', Ehrlich

[1] The German 'Physikum' is an equivalent of the first and second M.B., comprising Anatomy, Physiology, Physics, Chemistry, Botany and Zoology.

writes, 'that although I had not come to any of his lectures, I must have an extraordinary gift for chemistry. I really believe myself,' Ehrlich continues, 'that my talents lie in the field of chemistry; I can picture the chemical formulae in my mental vision and I believe that this fact has been of the greatest value to me in my studies. I had already then foreseen many things in pure chemistry which only came to be known much later.'

In Breslau an interesting event occurred about this time. One day a physician from the town of Wollstein in Silesia came to Breslau to demonstrate to the University professors there his investigations on the anthrax bacillus. The guest was shown through the different laboratories and was also taken to the bench where the student Ehrlich was working. Watching him, the guest was told:

'That is "little Ehrlich". He is very good at staining, but he will *never* pass his examinations.'

This visiting physician from Wollstein was none other than Robert Koch, whose name was soon to become famous throughout the world. In later years he was very often in contact with this same 'little Ehrlich' and worked successfully in close collaboration with him.

And 'little Ehrlich' did pass his examinations, in spite of the pessimistic prediction of his tutors.

In Leipzig, where he completed his University studies, he continued experimenting with dyes, and much of this was done in a little inn where he used to take his meals. Years later, when he had become famous throughout the world through his invention of 606, the daughter of the owners of that little inn wrote to Ehrlich reminding him of the time when all the towels in the guests' rooms and the billiard room in her parents' house were covered, to the despair of all concerned, with great spots of dye in every shade of red and blue which no amount of washing could remove. Even the billiard table itself, on which he had made his experiments because there was no other table, was covered with such spots.

It was at Leipzig that Ehrlich graduated in 1878, at the age of twenty-four, as a Doctor of Medicine. His degree thesis was based on his very first *analytical* studies of staining methods. It dealt with the value and significance in medicine of staining with aniline dyes.

Nobody seems to know anything about this thesis. Ehrlich himself did not remember what had become of it. It certainly was not printed. Only after his death did his wife and his friend Professor Leonor Michaelis of Berlin succeed in tracing the original. It was at last found in the archives of the University of Leipzig and bore the following title:[1] 'Contributions to the Theory and Practice of Histological Staining. Part I. The Chemical Conception of Staining. Part II. The Aniline Dyes from Chemical, Technological and Histological Aspects.' (Leipzig, 17 June, 1878.)

This paper is of great value in the study of Ehrlich's scientific development. In it he criticized the histologists because 'they cared so little for the *theory* of staining despite the fact that improvements in the practice of technical dyeing might well be expected to result from a correct theory.'[2]

Owing to the kindness of Professor Kruse, Dean of the Faculty of Medicine at the University of Leipzig, it has been possible for a copy of this remarkable document to be made. In the original manuscript, most of which was written in an unknown handwriting, were a large number of marginal notes, a recapitulation of contents, and a whole chapter in Ehrlich's own hand. These pages were written in Gothic characters, and Ehrlich must have taken a great deal of trouble to write them in this way. The marginal notes in the later part of the manuscript, on the other hand, were written in Roman script, and all without capital letters. Thus we see that even in his youth Ehrlich preferred his own peculiar style of handwriting, which became still more characteristic in later years. This manuscript already shows the large energetic character of his writing.

Professor Leonor Michaelis of Berlin, who searched for this document in the archives of Leipzig University, says about the thesis:

[1] 'Beiträge zur Theorie und Praxis der histologischen Färbung. I. Teil: Die chemische Auffassung der Färbung. II. Teil: Die Anilinfarben in chemischer, technologischer und histologischer Beziehung.' (Leipzig, 17 juni, 1878.)

[2] Since the manuscript of this biographical sketch was completed, I have discovered, in the library of the British Museum, the journal in which Ehrlich's first paper was published in 1877, the year before he presented the unpublished Inaugural-Dissertation. The subject is the same, and the earlier published paper presents, in more concise form, the main theme of the dissertation. In 1877 Ehrlich was still a young candidate in Medicine, aged twenty-three; it is remarkable to note how far, at that early age, he had begun to outline the ideas which were to guide so much of his later work.

'Paul Ehrlich has here defined his decided attitude towards
the purely chemical conception of the staining process; and, in
his reflections about the nature of staining, the *"idea of a chemical
binding of heterogeneous substances to the protoplasm"* was born. This
idea quite logically developed into his *Side-Chain Theory*; and for
this idea he fought all his life and in this fight made all his
discoveries. If we ask: "Was this idea right?"—different times
and different investigators will give different answers. Ideas
emerge, are forgotten, and are replaced by others. But for his
work the idea was necessary and useful. It was the light which
illuminated his way to new discoveries. He worked all his life to
prove that this idea was right, and in doing so he discovered
many facts which can never perish or disappear but will outlast
all Time.'[1]

Professor Julius Morgenroth, a former pupil and assistant of
Ehrlich, well known for his studies in Chemotherapy, to whom I
sent a copy of this thesis, wrote to me about it as follows:

'I am especially grateful to you for having made me acquainted with Ehrlich's dissertation. It is really astonishing,
even to those who realise that precocity is a distinguishing,
essential trait in the character of a genius. Here the fact is mani-
fested that great men with a mysterious inner power are im-
pelled by it into their own proper sphere of work. It is amazing
how many germs of later work there are in this paper by the
young Ehrlich, the form of which also shows, almost completely
developed, the characteristics of his style of writing.'

In 'The Book of the Great Chemists'[2] Dr. Richard Koch,
Professor of Medical History at the University of Frankfurt, says
about this dissertation:

'It contains the germ of Ehrlich's entire life-work which cul-
minated in the invention of Salvarsan. . . . It proves that Ehrlich, when leaving the University and before he even became a
clinical assistant, was already on the way to becoming the
creator of Chemotherapy. . . . This long-lost graduation thesis
undoubtedly belongs to the classical, epoch-making works of
medical world-literature. The ideas it contains are not nearly

[1] 'Zur Erinnerung an Paul Ehrlich: Seine wiedergefundene Doktordis-
sertation,' Von Prof. Dr. Leonor Michaelis (*Naturwissenschaften*, Heft 11, 14
März, 1919, S. 167).
[2] Bugge, 'Das Buch der Grossen Chemiker', 1929, Bd. II, S. 425 ff.

exhausted, and they allow us an insight into the scientific soul of
Paul Ehrlich which we cannot obtain in any other way. They
also give us the key to the chapter: "Paul Ehrlich as Chemist"[1]
... In 1877, the year before this dissertation, he had already
written on the same subject in the "Archives of Microscopic
Anatomy".'

What Ehrlich stated in this graduation thesis recurred again
and again in his later writings in one form or another, and ran
like a 'red strand' through all his publications.

[1] Paul Ehrlich, *Eine Darstellung seines wissenschattlichen Wirkens*, Kapitel E
'Chemie und Biochemie', p. 411-505. (Gustav Fischer, Jena, 14 März, 1914.)

CHAPTER III

AT THE CHARITÉ CLINIC, BERLIN

In the same year, 1878, Paul Ehrlich, at the age of twenty-four, passed his State Examination as a physician, and immediately after leaving the University, he became Assistant, and later on 'Oberarzt' or Senior House Physician, at the 2nd Medical Clinic of the Charité-Hospital in Berlin, under the direction of Professor von Frerichs.

'One went in the so-called laboratory', wrote one of Ehrlich's colleagues in a letter much later, 'through a dark entrance, stumbling over brooms, water-pails and boards which were used for tying out the bodies of dead animals for dissection. Along the walls of the laboratory were long shelves with glass vessels and small bottles filled with dyes. On one shelf there was nothing but two pots. There was an incubator and boards used for fixing objects for experimental purposes. On one of the boards a mouse was tied for examination. Then there was a long laboratory bench with a Bunsen burner and a water-tap . . . and that was the entire equipment.

'Paul Ehrlich pointed to the two pots on one of the shelves and said, laughingly:

' "My anatomical collection." He took down one of the pots and lifting the cover allowed his somewhat amused but none-the-less curious visitor to look into it. He introduced the specimen thus:

' "Here you see a rare piece of a cancer. . . ." Then he took out with forceps another specimen from the other pot, saying:

' "Here is an extirpated primary chancre[1] . . . wissen Sie . . . verstehen Sie . . . (you know, you understand) . . . when the microbe which causes syphilis is discovered, I must be prepared[2] . . ." and he gave a whimsical little laugh.'

[1] First ulcer in syphilis at the beginning of the disease.
[2] The spirochaete of syphilis was discovered more than twenty-five years later in 1905 by Professor Schaudinn of Vienna and Professor Hoffmann of Bonn, who were at that time working together at the Kaiserliches Gesundheitsamt, Berlin.

In his work at the Charité, Ehrlich had plenty of opportunity to make use of all the reactions he discovered, to continue his analytical study of dyes and to develop his skill in

Paul Ehrlich aged twenty-four

diagnosis, which was later so often praised. This freedom was
only possible because his chief, Professor von Frerichs, had
recognised from the very beginning the special ability of this
young assistant. He did not trouble him too much with everyday

clinical duties, but gave him a free hand to carry out his experiments.

Ehrlich at this time was always gay and cheerful, full of whims and fancies. Every morning he gave the order to the boy who helped him in the laboratory:

'Karl, a caviar sandwich . . .' and the boy ran off to bring back regularly a stale roll with a scanty scraping of butter and a very little dry ham upon it. Teased by his colleagues about this Ehrlich laughingly replied:

'My dear friends, you don't understand. . . . At the moment when I give the order I have at least the pleasure of illusory anticipation: the feeling that it *might* be, perhaps, just this once, a caviar sandwich. . . .'

Ehrlich already smoked a great deal, and Karl always had to get for him at a certain store in the Unter den Linden twenty cigars at fifty pfennig each—an enormous expense for a young assistant. When his colleagues remarked to Ehrlich that Karl might quite easily buy the cigars at forty or even twenty-five pfennig each and charge him fifty apiece for them, he replied:

'I have calculated exactly how much Karl is cheating me. If I gave him the sack and took another boy, his unfair profits would perhaps be even higher. *To figure this out would disturb me too much in my work!*'

So that he would always have cigars ready to hand, Ehrlich sometimes even took a cab and ordered the coachman to drive him to the cigar store in a hurry to get a fresh supply.

· · · · · ·

The two large wards in von Frerich's clinic were always filled with selected patients who were seriously ill, and it was often heart-rending to hear and see so many sick people in the large, overcrowded rooms. To be engaged under these conditions in exclusively clinical duties was, naturally, for a sensitive man like Ehrlich, well-nigh unbearable. And yet he never failed in the discharge of the heavy duties. His former colleague recalls that he performed the most delicate manipulations required for medical purposes, such as puncture of the liver of a patient with tabes to determine its glycogen content, and always, whatever he did was done with the utmost gentleness so as to hurt the patient as little as possible. On one occasion, when it became necessary to do a tracheotomy on a young girl unexpectedly, he held the tracheal-wound open with a fork until the cannula was fetched from the surgical clinic.

Every day after the morning rounds the urine of almost all the patients had to be examined with Ehrlich's diazo-reaction in the laboratory, and according to the result the prognosis was

Professor von Frerichs

made. With his special training and experience in the use of this reaction, Ehrlich could frequently predict from the urine of a patient with typhoid fever a critical change for the worse, even though no alarming symptoms had yet been observed. Often his colleagues were doubtful and would not believe him, but the further course of the illness always proved him right.

Then blood preparations had to be stained. Ehrlich's reputation as an expert stainer caused a number of eager and zealous students to come to him—he had in the meantime also become a lecturer at the University—to learn his methods. In making blood preparations Ehrlich required that his methods should be followed exactly to the last detail, and anyone who deviated from them was exposed to severe criticism. He himself was inde-fatigable in his work, and his perseverance caused his pupils to invent the saying: 'Ehrlich färbt am längsten' (Ehrlich goes on longest with his staining), a parody of the proverb (Ehrlich währt am längsten' (Honesty lasts longest, i.e. honesty is the best policy).

Well-known University professors came to visit Ehrlich, sometimes every day, and it was very amusing to see the astonishment, at the accuracy and perfection of his work, of those who had no previous knowledge of the primitive nature of his working equipment. It pleased Ehrlich especially to see a new visitor at his experimenting table. There was on one side of this table a tripod on which lay an iron plate, larger than the tripod. Under the protruding end of this iron plate there was a Bunsen burner. Ehrlich would show this arrangement laugh-ingly and say:

'This is my equipment for staining blood preparations . . . wissen Sie . . . verstehen Sie.'

He heats the iron plate over the tripod with the gas jet. Then he puts some water from the tap into a test tube and makes drops of the water fall on to the heated iron plate, which hisses.

'You see . . . at the place where the drops of water boil, we have 100° C. Then'—he puts a few glass slides with blood films on the heated end of the plate—'the blood preparations are slightly heated . . . fixed'—he picks up one of the glass slides with forceps and puts it carefully into a small bowl of dye-solution which stands near, followed by the other slides, one after the other—'and stained'.

'Inspired, simply inspired!' the visitor can only stammer, full of admiration. Then Ehrlich is asked:

'What is happening to your paper on "The Organism in Need of Oxygen"? How is it going?'

He is already busy with some other work, and answers only with a little jerk of his head towards one of the shelves on the wall, on the farthest end of which lies a pile of manuscript, and says, without looking up from his experiments:

'Soon . . . during the vacation . . .'

While he continues to work he quotes from this new publication, which is shortly to appear and the news of which has
already been causing a sensation:

'Exactly *how* the dye gets into the cell I am not yet sure, but
there can be no doubt that its entry into the cell is dependent
on the size of the molecule. I imagine it must be so. Just as

Hedwig Pinkus, Ehrlich's Bride, aged nineteen

meteors penetrate into the gaseous atmosphere of the earth, so
molecules of the smallest size are projected into the plasma of
the cell and remain there, useful in some way or another (as
oxygen-carriers for instance), and then are again eliminated.' [1]

But the publication of this important monograph had still to
wait a while: It was not prepared for the printers during the
vacation. For, first of all, Ehrlich married the charming nine-

[1] From Ehrlich's monograph 'Das Sauerstoffbedürfnis des Organismus'.
Eine farbenanalytische Studie, Berlin, Hirschwald, 1885.

teen-year-old daughter of a family connected with one of the important industries of Upper Silesia. She was Hedwig Pinkus of Neustadt, and in her he found a lovely, faithful and understanding companion for the rest of his life.

Ehrlich's scientific work during this period as a young assistant was enormous. The magnitude of his accomplishments in medical science is hardly comprehensible to an ordinary observer. The roots of all his later successful work for the benefit of mankind are to be found in these early discoveries. While still a young man he achieved fame as a pioneer in scientific quarters all over the world, and his work was invariably directed towards the goal of increasing knowledge of biological data and so increasing knowledge of diseases and how to cure them. Not having passed through a really orthodox medical or chemical curriculum in his university course, having spent his time even as a student, as we have seen, in following those ideas of his own which reappear at all stages of his life's work, he never created a 'school' of his own in the conventional sense of the word. But from all parts of the world young scientific investigators came to learn his methods. They entered enthusiastically into his particular field of work and ideas, and carried his teaching with them when they returned to their own countries.

.   .   .   .   .   .

At this juncture in Ehrlich's career came the momentous discovery of the tubercle bacillus by Robert Koch. This sensational event was announced by Koch himself in a lecture at the meeting of the Physiological Society of Berlin in 1882.

During this lecture Ehrlich remembered that, in his own experiments on staining preparations of organs and sputa from patients with tuberculosis, he had once seen some isolated rod-shaped bacteria for which he could find no explanation at the time. Immediately after the lecture he hastened to his laboratory at the Charité and began to experiment with dyes.

There was in his laboratory a small iron stove in which the fire had been out for hours. He found it handy now, because it was already late at night, and he could not easily find a suitable stand. So he put the stained preparations on the iron top of the stove in order to dry.

The next morning the woman who cleaned the laboratory lit

the fire in the little stove, without seeing the glass slides which were lying on top of it.

Ehrlich came into the laboratory early, in great haste to look at the preparations. Seeing the fire in the stove he rushed forward, terrified. Taking up the slides and holding them against

Paul Ehrlich aged twenty-nine

the light he observed to his astonishment that they were wonderfully stained, and on examining them under the microscope he found the tubercle bacilli standing out in them in clumps. A strange accident had thus come to his aid, or, to use Ehrlich's own expression, 'Glück' (luck)—one of his 'Big G's'—which he always said were necessary for successful work. In this case the warmth of the iron top of the stove had assisted the process of staining and produced this remarkable result, which provided a

starting point for a multitude of important studies of tuberculosis.

Ehrlich immediately hastened to see Robert Koch and show
him what he had discovered, and at once the most intensive
work in this new field of research began. Koch, in a publication[1] on this subject later, recognised the great importance of
Ehrlich's specific staining of the tubercle bacilli. He said:

'It was soon found that, with Ehrlich's method of staining, the
recognition of tubercle bacilli could readily be made use of in
diagnosis. We owe it to this circumstance alone that it has
become a general custom to search for the bacillus in sputum,
whereas, without it, it is likely that but few investigators would
have concerned themselves with tubercle bacilli.'

A result of Robert Koch's work was the development of a
purely etiological line of investigation, the object of which was
to search for and discover the *causes* of disease. This profoundly
interested Ehrlich. He joined in the work, and through their
common interest in this line of research there began a closer
co-operation between him and Robert Koch. Soon Koch called
upon Ehrlich, together with Dr. P. Gutmann, to undertake the
first treatments of patients with tuberculin in the Moabit
Hospital in Berlin, and to watch the results.

. . . . . .

The sudden death of Professor von Frerichs, Ehrlich's kindly
chief at the Charité, was a heavy blow to him. A successor came,
Professor Gerhardt, who was not so broad-minded as his predecessor and did not understand Ehrlich. He wished to force the
young assistant into the rigid routine of clinical medicine, and
did not recognise the importance of Ehrlich's research work.
This is clearly shown by an incident which occurred one day in
the clinic. For the sake of a demonstration to the students, the
patients suffering from typhoid fever were to be kept in a
medium state of fever with suitably spaced doses of Thalline,
which Ehrlich called 'continuous Thallinisation'. Professor Gerhardt spoke critically of Ehrlich to another assistant, saying:

'Ehrlich will only spoil the typical form of the fever-curve
which we need for the demonstration.'

He had simply not understood the meaning of Ehrlich's

[1] Deutsche Medizinische Wochenschrift 1883, No. 10.

researches, and Ehrlich could not stand for long the constant strain of work under these conditions. He began, further, to show signs of pulmonary tuberculosis, acquired in the course of his clinical work. Accordingly, he resigned from his position at the Charité Hospital and went to Egypt with his young wife, remaining there for two years until he had recovered from the disease.

In the opinion of his friends, his tuberculosis was not very serious, but his health threatened to break down completely because of the psychological strain he had to endure. His cousin, Professor Felix Pinkus of Berlin, commented on this in an obituary notice after Ehrlich's death,[1] saying:

'Ehrlich's mind could not bear any bonds. Just as a highly-strung racehorse would end by quivering helplessly in the yoke, breaking down as a result of nervous excitement without advancing or making any effective effort, so Ehrlich's body would pine away when his spirit was fettered. Once, more than twenty-five years ago, we feared for his life. After the sudden death of his patron and friend von Frerichs, the greatest disaster which had befallen Ehrlich, he was forced into drudgery, was compelled to march the old road of clinical routine. He could not endure this, and visibly began to fade away until he had to free himself in order to save his life. His illness was called tuberculosis of the lungs, and he had the clinical symptoms of that disease. But what he was suffering from mostly was constraint. The easily cured tuberculosis never troubled him again, when once he had recovered his strength.'

In his autobiographical notes already mentioned, Ehrlich wrote about this trying time:

'When I felt so miserable and forsaken during the time with Gerhardt, I often stood before the cupboard in which my collection of dyes was stored and said to myself: "These here are my friends which will not desert me" . . .'

1 Medizinische Klinik 1915, No. 50/51.

CHAPTER IV

RESEARCH WITH ROBERT KOCH
AND EMIL VON BEHRING

AFTER his return from Egypt in 1889, strong and healthy again, Ehrlich set up a little private laboratory in Berlin and con-

Robert Koch

tinued to work out his own ideas successfully, although only on a small scale and at his own expense.

Koch in the meantime had taken in hand the direction of the newly founded Institute for Infectious Diseases (Institut für Infectionskrankheiten Robert Koch) in Berlin. He offered Ehrlich a place in his Institute where he could work, and Ehrlich

gladly accepted and transferred his researches to the Robert
Koch Institute.

Then followed, as his contemporaries agreed in their publications, a new phase in Ehrlich's work: bacteriology.

'This was the line of thought and research on which Ehrlich
had for such a long time been working and for which he fought
unceasingly: to discover chemical compounds which, on account
of their chemical relationships to certain cells and substances of
the organism, are carried to these parts, distributed and
"anchored" there, and thus have an efficient specific influence
there, and only there.'

At this time Ehrlich began to work with Emil von Behring,
and from their active co-operation a close friendship developed.

In 1892 Emil von Behring discovered specific immune substances in the blood-serum of animals which had been infected
with diphtheria or tetanus bacilli.

The whole world was excited about this discovery, and with
the highest hopes the diphtheria-antitoxin, the serum that was to
cure diphtheria, was introduced into medical treatment. The
results, however, were disappointing. It was found that the
antitoxin in Behring's serum was not strong enough to bring
about the desired effect. The research was threatened with complete failure; for unless the remedy could be made to work, it
would have to be discarded, and it would appear that the discovery had led to false conclusions and was of little value.

At this point Ehrlich set to work to give his friend von Behring
the benefit of his scientific experience and to help him make his
specific serum really useful and effective. In extensive experiments on animals he worked out a precise method of measuring
the curative value of the antitoxin in units defined in relation to
a fixed standard. A serum rich in antitoxin was thus produced
in the blood of horses as the result of repeated inoculations. The
strength of this serum rose higher and higher and attained a
trustworthy degree of potency as a remedy for diphtheria. The
standards which Ehrlich set up were eventually accepted everywhere, and antidiphtheritic serum, as now produced throughout the world, is standardised in terms of the units which he
defined for the indication of its specific potency.

Professor Julius Morgenroth, assistant and follower of Ehrlich, said in an article about the research work on diphtheria:

'Although Behring's discovery was clear and unquestionable in its fundamental principles much, almost everything, was wanting to render it a reliable, trustworthy and permanent advance in medical treatment. Then Ehrlich intervened with his great experience, and as the result of their united efforts the

Emil von Behring

diphtheria serum was perfected and made useful in practical therapy.

'To Ehrlich is due the credit of having created biological methods of measuring the antitoxins (those curative substances, produced by Nature itself, to-day still of unknown composition and obstinately defying the efforts of chemists), and of determining quantitatively the curative value of antidiphtheritic serum in terms of its antitoxin-content. The whole structure of

Serum-Therapy to-day stands on the basis of his exact method of measurement, which is used now throughout the world for determining the value of curative sera.'

.   .   .   .   .

Because of the close co-operation which existed between Ehrlich and von Behring, the chemical factory which had declared itself ready to produce the diphtheria-serum for general medical use made a contract with both these investigators, to give them a percentage of the financial returns from this discovery. This unfortunately turned out to be one of the greatest disappointments which Ehrlich ever experienced, a really tragic disillusionment, to which he never became fully reconciled. In letters which Ehrlich later wrote, his own ideas and feelings concerning what happened as the result of these negotiations are very emphatically recorded. One day he received an urgent telegram from the chemical works, asking him to go immediately to the town of Halle-on-Saale (about two hours' journey from Berlin) to discuss some clauses of the contract. A representative of the factory and Emil von Behring were waiting for him when he arrived.

Von Behring and the factory representative spoke about Ehrlich's future plans, and he was, of course, extremely pleased by the prospect of being able to spend more freely on his research work, as the necessary means would come to him as the result of his contract. In a letter to one of his friends, many years later, Ehrlich estimated that these returns would have been at least thirty to forty thousand marks a year for a minimum period of fourteen years, that is to say, more than half a million marks.

In the course of this conversation von Behring spoke of one of Ehrlich's favourite ideas. This was to work in a State Institute for Research where he could, as Director, be completely free to act according to his own ideas and plans. Von Behring promised his friend that he, von Behring, now being highly esteemed by the Government authorities, would use all his influence to get Ehrlich appointed to such a position. But of course, as he pointed out, as Director of a State Institute Ehrlich would not be allowed to accept any money from a chemical factory. He carefully explained, with the assistance of the factory representative, that, in the event of such good fortune, Ehrlich would have to resign from his contract with the factory. . . .

Between them they contrived to bring Ehrlich, naturally given to ready enthusiasm, into a state of great excitement, in which he was carried away by an ecstasy of happiness. As if in a trance, he paid no attention to the 'whens' and 'buts' of the others. He did not hear the remark of the chemical-factory representative that, really, a 'double burden' upon the budget of the factory, caused by the participation of *both* investigators, would be 'insupportable'.

Emil von Behring was unable to keep his promise to help Ehrlich obtain an appointment as Director of a State Institute —the dream of his life—where he could be completely free to act in research work according to his own ideas and plans. Apparently von Behring's influence was not sufficiently great to do this, but none-the-less he was able to build himself a castle on the heights surrounding Marburg-on-Lahn, with a mausoleum in the castle garden for himself and his family; and he was able to establish the 'Behring-Works' there and to maintain them from his income.

Relations of formal politeness between Ehrlich and von Behring were eventually renewed and maintained. But the great gap between them remained. They never saw each other again.

.   .   .   .   .

A significant event, though belonging to a much later period, must be here anticipated: at the height of his success, after the invention of 606, Ehrlich got hundreds of letters asking for his autograph. A specially enthusiastic autograph-hunter even sent his entire album filled with the autographs of famous people, and asked Ehrlich to add to it his well-known chemotherapeutical axiom 'Corpora non agunt nisi fixata' and his name. I shall never forget Ehrlich's profound emotion when I called his attention to a page on which was written:

> 'Der Erfolg entscheidet   (Success decides
> Ueber Recht und Unrecht   whether right or wrong
> Ueber Gut und Schlecht.'   whether good or bad.)
> *Emil von Behring.*

to which he remarked: 'Quite characteristic!' An unknown person had written the following fine answer beneath:

> 'Der Anbeter des Erfolges   (He who worships success
> Kann die Welt   Can make the world
> Nicht gut noch glücklich   Neither good nor happy.)
> machen.'

And when on 20 August, 1915, Ehrlich had passed away, Emil von Behring came to Frankfurt to take part in the funeral ceremony. He followed with difficulty in the funeral procession, an aged, sick man, his hand resting heavily upon his cane. He had written a touching obituary which he published later. But here in the face of death, at the open tomb, he could but stammer these few words:

> 'Nun ruhest auch Du, Du lieber Freund . . .
> Du hattest stets eine empfindliche Seele . . .
> Und wenn wir Dir wehgetan haben . . . Verzeih!'

> (Now you are at rest, my dear friend . . .
> You always had a sensitive soul . . .
> And if we have hurt you . . . forgive us!)

.   .   .   .   .

Official relations, however, had to continue between them, because the Serum Institute at Steglitz, of which Ehrlich was made Director in 1896, and later his Institute at Frankfurt, were responsible for the State Control of all sera; and von Behring's antidiphtheritic serum had, of course, to pass through this control. Behring regretted that he had lost Ehrlich's friendship and collaboration, and he tried several times in a roundabout way to obtain his help in the problems of his new research work. But Ehrlich refused to be exploited again.

In a letter written on 27 November, 1899, to a friend in Copenhagen who inquired about this, Ehrlich said:

'I am not surprised at what you tell me about B——g. He has reaped as he sowed. He did not mention at that time that the Institute of which he originally spoke would be a subsidiary of Marburg, and I his employee. But later on he seems to have had the idea that I should work for him for a small wage and help *him* to find new discoveries and make millions! He owes his success with the diphtheria serum, especially his big material success, to *me*. When we started to work together his serum contained only $\frac{1}{4}$ to $\frac{1}{2}$ a unit of antitoxin per c.c., while mine had thirty. I had worked with ruminants, goats and cows, whereas he had used horses which give much stronger antitoxins. When, with great difficulty and after nearly nine months of hard work, he had, by using my methods, reached 100–150 units, he tried to bring me into discredit, pretending that I knew nothing about immunisation and that he obtained a much higher unitage than I did, etc. He deliberately refrained from saying that this depended on the kind of animal used. I had by that time brought my goats to yield 100 units, which means a very *high* immunity, as everyone who has worked with goats is aware.

'I always get wild whenever I think of that dark period and the way in which B. tried to hide our scientific partnership. But the revenge has come. He can see how far he has got without me since our separation. Everything is blocked now: his work on plague, cholera, glanders, streptococcal infections. He makes no progress with diphtheria—only hypotheses of a daring kind and a pseudo-exact manipulation of numbers. And all this with more than sufficient means in hand, and a swarm of collaborators— Ruppel, Lingelsheim, Knorr, Japanese workers and the assistance of the big factory.

'Of course, you can imagine how filled with rage he is. He wanted to be the "All-Highest" who would dictate his laws to the entire world and who, in addition, could earn the most money. He wanted to be a Superman; but—thank God—he did not have the necessary super-brain. The "Berglaboratorium" (mountain laboratory) with its halls, ponds, meadows, etc. was conceived by him as a fortress of science; but it is very fortunate for the free investigator that this plan has been destroyed; that instead of being a temple where he could be worshipped . . . it is just a normal laboratory. Away with the mammonisation of science!'

Von Behring continued to trouble Ehrlich throughout the years. He was of the opinion that Ehrlich's Institute at Frankfurt ought, by rights, to undertake without charge all the experimental control work which he, von Behring, wanted done. He appealed to the German Government to order Ehrlich to accept this obligation. When Ehrlich was asked about this, he made an extensive report to the Prussian Ministry, explaining that this would be impossible; and in a long, fourteen-page letter dated 1 November, 1906, to Dr. Althoff, his patron, Director of the Prussian Ministry of Ecclesiastical, Educational and Medical Affairs,[1] he said:

'To explain this matter correctly I must refer to the early history of the Institute. My work on Immunity was begun quite independently of von Behring's and had brought to light the

[1] (Direktor im Ministerium für Geistliche, Kultur- und Medizinal-Angelegenheiten.)

fact that an immunity exists against the albuminous poisons of plants (Ricin, Abrin). I was the first to follow this up quantitatively and I found that it could be *progressively* increased by appropriate methods. When von Behring's discovery of the antitoxins was announced, my collaborators (especially Wassermann) and I started to apply my principles concerning the increase of immunity to this subject. Beginning with tetanus and then going on to the immunisation against diphtheria which was more practically important, we set to work to produce a very high immunity and to use the *milk* of the treated animals ("Immune milk") in therapeutic experiments. . . . This was in sharp competition with von Behring, who had not succeeded in making his important discovery of the antitoxins practically useful. When—I believe it was in the autumn of 1901—trial treatments were carried out with Behring's serum in the children's ward of a hospital, no positive results were obtained. In fact it was impossible that they should be, for his serum contained in 1 c.c. considerably less than 1 unit and could not produce any action. Thereupon I was asked to make experiments with my serum which immediately gave good results; for my sera (obtained from goats, difficult animals to use for immunisation) had 30 units in 1 c.c. One serum had almost 100 units in 1 c.c.

'It was in these circumstances that von Behring asked me to collaborate with him, and indeed this may have been necessary for him, for in spite of all the means which the Höchst factory placed at his disposal, he made no progress at all in his experiments. He was entirely on the wrong track, thinking that *hypersensitive* animals must be brought to a high degree of immunity with the smallest possible doses. He had also completely disregarded the absolute necessity of producing a *very strong toxin*, which is the pivotal point of all attempts to get a high grade of immunity. When we began working together he showed me a bottle containing five quarts of diphtheria toxin. He believed that this would be sufficient for fifty years immunisation work in a large factory. It would hardly have been enough for one horse! On the other hand, my collaborators and I were convinced of the necessity of using progressively increasing doses of a very active toxin, in order to obtain the desired increase of immunity. It was difficult to get von Behring to accept my point of view and my methods, and to set him on the right track; but then, after more than six months of experimenting, he really succeeded in producing active sera. At first he had nothing that could be used; and he could not give a single drop of serum for the fundamental experiments, made especially by Professor Kossel in the Berlin hospitals, to find out the proper curative and immunising doses.

'So it was *I* who, at this *critical* time, straightened out the confusion and put von Behring on the right lines which enabled him to achieve success with his discovery.

'And when he finally arrived at this point and was covered with honour and glory, his first deed was to rob me of the rewards of many years of work . . .'

Ehrlich then gave the details of the way in which he was tricked by von Behring out of the contract with the chemical works. The report then continued:

'I still feel very bitter whenever I think of this time, not because of the heavy material loss, which no longer troubles me, but because of the unfriendly way in which von Behring carried out his plans. I put him in the saddle and he responded by knocking me down. He disliked my help, although it was necessary. . . . I consider it the height of injustice that von Behring should claim that a part of the income of my Institute should be used to help him in his personal investigations. It has always been *he* who profited from our collaboration.

'I have an utter dread of a real collaboration with von Behring. In the diphtheria period, reported above, there was a constant scientific struggle between us. I came out of it victorious, but it was a Pyrrhic victory, only gained after much anger and complete exhaustion. . . .

'In my Berlin Institute at Steglitz I had to work with him again. Von Behring believed that he had found, by treating tubercle bacilli under high temperatures, a very active preparation for the treatment of tuberculosis. He said this preparation would very soon be ready to be put into production commercially by the Höchst factory. Professor Dönitz made the animal experiments and found that all the animals died from bacterial infection, and that this could only be avoided by the utmost precaution in making the injections. He found that it took half-an-hour to an hour to make such an injection properly, but that, if this care was taken, the preparation was not at all toxic. But von Behring, instead of being grateful to my Institute for having spared him a complete failure, was dissatisfied with our work. . . .

'The third time I had to work with von Behring was at Frankfurt. He thought that the control of tetanus-toxin, which was carried out at the Frankfurt Institute in a laborious but absolutely reliable way, could be simplified by the use of a liquid "test-toxin" which he said he had prepared. He said this could be used freely by anyone, thus making the control of the Serum Institute unnecessary. In the catalogue of the World Exhibition in Paris (1900) von Behring said: "The Frankfurt method of control, besides being laborious, also needs improvement for other reasons. There is no certainty of the absolutely stable character of the antitoxic test-preparations. And furthermore the possible errors caused by any instability of the toxic preparations may be reduced by the aforesaid control, but they cannot be excluded entirely. With a test-preparation of a stable character the measurement of antitoxic sera would, of course, be much simpler and much more reliable. My Tetanus Test-Toxin No. Va is a toxic liquid which contains preservatives and has remained constant for such a long period that I am justified in saying that it is of an almost ideal stability."

'But after the preparation was tested at the Frankfurt Institute these claims could not be substantiated. When the toxins arrived they showed values which were different from those von Behring had given us, and it was presumed in Marburg that they had been oxidised in transport. The testing of one preparation was hurried by the next one following almost on top of it, and the Frankfurt Institute was so upset by the extra and unnecessary work that I had to ask you at that time to put an end to it.

'Finally the test-toxin was tested and studied in Paris, and it was found there that it was completely oxidised. After that no more was said about it.

'Similar disturbances are to be feared if we are expected to undertake to a large extent the experimental scientific control of von Behring's new preparations. I have given the Minister a report on von Behring's cures with "Tulase", and called his attention to the fact that this treatment, the principal characteristic of which is the use of a "hundred-per-cent-tubercle-preparation", cannot be called an original invention by von

Behring; for Robert Koch outlined this programme long ago, and von Behring has simply worked upon it to perfect it.'

A detailed account of tubercle preparations in general then followed. The report continued:

'Less than a year has elapsed since von Behring gave a report at the last Congress on his different remedies for the treatment of tuberculosis. But during this time four new preparations have been recommended by him and have made their appearance: the "T.C.", "Tuberkulase", "Tulase" and "Tulon". To try out all these preparations thoroughly during the course of a single year would occupy a scientific research institute completely. There would be hardly any time left for other work.

'In my opinion the proper duty of a control institute is to test scientifically, according to the methods which the inventor has worked out, preparations which he intends later on to place under the State Control. These preparations should only be those which the inventor himself has definitely found to have a curative action. Such scientific control experiments have been made by us with every new preparation, and the expenses for this have been borne by my Institute. But I do not think the Institute should undertake part of the preliminary experimental work to discover an effective preparation and so relieve the inventor of work which he should do himself. Neither the staff nor the accommodation at the Institute would be sufficient to cope with such a task. Besides, I know from my previous experience of work with von Behring that it would mean a perpetual rush to keep up with the rapid change of preparations. Extensive series of animal experiments are planned with great care, and before these are finished we are told that meanwhile something newer and better has been found which must be tried out immediately, etc. etc.

'There is, as I have shown, no valid reason for von Behring's demand that the Institute should do the control work for him without charge. Such a demand is quite unjustified, for the Institute and the State Control Station must remain independent and distinct from all private concerns as hitherto, and cannot appear to be a branch of any other scientific institution. Any change in this direction would seriously damage the reputation of my Institute. If any such change occurred, in all probability the Chemical Works at Höchst, which has to pay by far the largest amounts for control tax, would demand the same privileges also.

'If, as he hopes, von Behring succeeds with his preparations, he will be amply rewarded, and the control taxes and other expenses connected with the testing experiments will not count at all in the end. Every manufacturer, every business or industrial establishment, must bear such expenses and make financial sacrifices in order to start a really promising enterprise which will lead to success in the future.'

Largely as a result of Ehrlich's letter, from which these extracts are taken, von Behring's application was rejected by the Ministry. This refusal to grant his requests did not, of course, improve his feelings towards Ehrlich.

CHAPTER V

THE STEGLITZ INSTITUTE

In 1884, five years before his formal admission as a University lecturer, Ehrlich had been made a titular professor, a distinction which was very rare at that time. But, as one of his friends said:

'The German University Medical Faculties did not for fifteen years put his name on any list of favoured candidates for a University Chair. In the end this could be regarded as having done him an unintentional service; for the man who was to cause such a revolutionary advance over the whole field of biological knowledge was forced from the hospital wards and lecture rooms into the research laboratory.'

But these laboratory researches had, meanwhile, to be paid for very largely out of Ehrlich's own pocket, especially when, coming back from Egypt to Berlin after recovering from his tuberculosis, he started a small laboratory of his own. Then, as has already been mentioned, Robert Koch offered him a place where he could work in his new Institute, and in every way Koch furthered the work of that 'little Ehrlich' of Breslau 'who could do first-class staining, but will never pass his examinations.' This lasted until 1896, when the Director of the Prussian Ministry of Educational and Medical Affairs, Dr. Althoff, a man who did much to further the work of German Universities in general, invited Ehrlich to become Director of the small 'State Institute for the Investigation and Control of Sera',[1] which was about to be opened in Steglitz, a suburb of Berlin, to establish a control by the Prussian State of diphtheria-serum and other newly found sera.

Dr. Althoff's invitation was accepted with alacrity, and thus Ehrlich's ardent desire to become head of an institute for medical research was fulfilled. But what kind of fulfilment was it?

Unlike Emil von Behring, who could run his 'Behring-

[1] Staatliches Institut für Serumforschung und Serumprüfung.

Werke' as he liked, and had at his disposal almost limitless means to bring about his wishes, Ehrlich had to do his research work restricted by a limited State budget. He could carry on only with great deficits which could not be liquidated without considerable difficulty, and often only after having made special

Dr. Althoff

appeals to the Government. Ehrlich had to work under very primitive conditions, in a disused bakehouse which had fallen out of repair, with an old stable close by for the animals. However, despite all these restrictions, he was happy. He had re-gained his optimism and faith, and worked ceaselessly, with unfailing physical energy and elasticity of mind, at his in-numerable tasks and problems. His theories led always to new plans and projects, far exceeding the limits of his essential daily duties. His tasks increased and his aims became higher and higher.

Every morning when he arrived at the Institute he would call for his boy Fritz, who hurried from the stable, prepared for his work in a big blue apron, and brought his master the cages containing the animals for experimental treatment.

Visitors coming to see him there were kindly welcomed. Let us watch Ehrlich at work one day when, as so often happens, he has a visitor. Hardly looking up from his experiments over the

Steglitz Institute for Serum Research and Control

Bunsen burner, he greets his visitor by holding out to him the little finger of his left hand, and saying, with his Silesian accent:

'Tag ook, lieber Kollege . . . was gib'ts Neues?' (Morning, dear Colleague . . . anything new?)

His light brown, bow-legged dachshund 'Männe', trotting in behind Fritz, sniffs at the strange visitor and immediately runs to his master, hovering round his feet. Ehrlich introduces the dog to his colleague with an amused laugh as 'the protector of the deficit'.

The visitor looks inquiringly round the scantily equipped laboratory and remarks:

'Well, Ehrlich, you know, the aspect of your laboratory is not at all imposing!'

Ehrlich is busily engaged pouring the dye solution he has been heating in a test tube over the Bunsen burner on to a large sheet of white blotting-paper which hangs from the big working-bench, and is prevented from falling by bottles of dye used as weights along its upper edge.

'As long as I have a water-tap, a flame and some blotting-paper', he says merrily, with a little nod towards the old stable, 'I can work just as well in a barn.'

Meanwhile Fritz has taken off his big blue apron which identifies him as an 'animal nurse', has washed, brushed and disinfected his hands, and then put on a clean white overall, to show that he is also a 'laboratory assistant'.

When Ehrlich has finished his experiment over the Bunsen burner he turns down the flame, looks at the spots on the blotting-paper, makes his conclusions from them, and then shows and explains to the visitor his primitive equipment. Then he calls out:

'Fritz, the animals . . . how is Hamilkar to-day?'

He takes one of the animals which Fritz shows him, examines it closely and puts it back into the cage. He nods, satisfied:

'That's going on all right!' Then, taking the second animal: 'I don't like the look of Hasdrubal. Take care, Fritz!'—and taking the third one: 'Hannibal can have another injection to-day.'

At the mention of these well-known names, the visitor finds it impossible to keep a straight face. He bursts out laughing and says:

'The Carthaginian Wars in Medicine!' to which Ehrlich responds with a smile.

Fritz, according to routine, takes a syringe from the steriliser and puts it on the table, with cotton wool and a solution for disinfection purposes. Meanwhile Ehrlich has put the animal in a high mouse jar, washed and disinfected his hands, prepared the solution for the injection and, when the injection has been given and Fritz is putting the animal back into the cage, says to him:

'Keep it under close observation—show it to me to-morrow.'

Ehrlich and his colleague then have a long and interesting

talk about Ehrlich's important new medical publication which is soon to appear. From an adjacent laboratory Dr. Dönitz and Dr. Max Neisser, who worked in collaboration with Ehrlich and were in charge of the current control of the sera sent in from the factories for examination, come in to ask their chief for advice on some important scientific questions. Queries and explanations are exchanged, and when the two have left the room again the visitor, full of astonished admiration, exclaims:

'It is really incredible, my dear Ehrlich, how you work, and how much you work!' Then, having reflected a moment, he adds: 'But that seems to be the way with all people of genius who work, prodigiously, without knowing it.'

To this Ehrlich replies, seriously and kindly:

'One simply has to, one is urged by some force from within.'

Then finally the visitor departs, and Ehrlich accompanies him to the door. Music is coming from the courtyard. A man has arrived with his barrel-organ and has taken up his stand in the middle of the courtyard on the rough stone pavement from which tufts of grass are sprouting. He turns the handle and out come the popular songs of that time: 'Mother, the man with the coke is here', 'Oh, come down, oh Madonna Theresa', 'On the green banks of the Spree', and such like. He comes regularly, at least once every week, and always receives a good reward to induce him to play as much as possible.

'Now you see, dear Colleague, how well I am cared for. Now I can work wonderfully', says Ehrlich to his departing guest, and laughing in good humour he goes back to his work.

Ehrlich loved this simple music and other light and gay tunes. He always said that with such music around him he could do his best work. When he was a schoolboy at College in Breslau there was a boy called Fritz Leubuscher, the son of a Breslau merchant family, who was also a boarder in the house of Dr. Munck at the same time as young Ehrlich.

One of his former comrades in a private letter to a friend wrote:

'Fritz was a great teaser, but he fascinated young Paul with his violin-playing. Fritz knew that; and often, when he had irritated Paul to the limit with his teasing, he would suddenly take up his instrument and play a little song. As soon as he

E

began to play Paul would become calm, and by the end he
would be joyfully dancing around.'

    .   .   .   .   .

It is almost impossible to realise how hard Ehrlich worked
during the time he was at Steglitz. One publication followed

Paul Ehrlich aged forty-two

another, and all were of the greatest significance in scientific
and practical medicine.

An idea of his untiring energy may be gained by the fact that
between the years of 1877 and 1914 he published 232 papers and
books and thus contributed very greatly to the literature of
science. He also inspired the publication of more than four hun-

dred articles by his collaborators and assistants, while thousands of articles by chemists, clinicians and research workers all over the world resulted indirectly from his scientific knowledge and intuition.

It is not surprising, therefore, that Dr. Althoff, Ehrlich's patron in the Ministry, confronted by such genius, such im-

Dr. Franz Adickes, Lord Mayor of Frankfurt am Main

mense and untiring energy and such positive views on the most important scientific problems of the day, came to realise that this young investigator ought to be given the opportunity to work on a much wider scale than any which was possible in the primitively equipped and poorly endowed Steglitz Institute.

Dr. Althoff found a willing promotor of his plans in the Lord Mayor of Frankfurt am Main, Dr. Adickes, who had been largely responsible for increasing the size and economic importance of Frankfurt. Between them they succeeded in bringing about the foundation of the large 'Institute for Experimental Therapy' at Frankfurt am Main which was to be an extension of the Steglitz Institute and was opened three years later (in 1899) with Ehrlich as Director. There he was destined to work for sixteen years, until the end of his life, and there he made most of the great discoveries and inventions by which he so largely contributed to the progress of medical science and to the welfare of mankind.

CHAPTER VI

THE FRANKFURT 'SERUM-INSTITUTE'

Königlich Preussisches Institut für experimentelle Therapie
(Royal Prussian Institute for Experimental Therapy)

THE new Institute for Experimental Therapy, in which Ehrlich was going to work and plan as Director, was erected far out in South Frankfurt, near the Hospital Buildings which in later years were to become an assembly of University Clinics when the University of Frankfurt was founded.

In former times, before it became a part of Frankfurt, this whole district on the left bank of the Main was called Sachsenhausen, beyond which, having passed the outskirts of the town, one came to the 'Gerbermühle', i.e., Tanner's Mill, Goethe's well-known favourite retreat. Friedrich Stoltze, the local nineteenth-century poet of Frankfurt, used mockingly to call Sachsenhausen 'dribb der Bach', while of Frankfurt itself he would say 'hibb der Bach', meaning that Frankfurt was situated on the 'correct' side of the Main, and Sachsenhausen on the 'wrong' side. The Main he called a 'Bach', a brook.

The front of the new scientific institute dominated the Sandhofstrasse, a broad suburban street with pretty country villas, gardens and building-plots with trees and grass. In the rear it had a view on one side of the hospital buildings surrounded by a park-like garden, and in the far distance the hills of the Taunus, with the Feldberg as their highest point. Away from the noisy city, with its little front garden filled with lilacs, red hawthorn and maple trees, it was a quiet, ideal working place.

At the entrance a few steps led up past the two rooms occupied by the porter, Kadereit. Dr. Althoff of Berlin had recommended Kadereit to Ehrlich as being the most trustworthy person he could have around him, and he had become Ehrlich's 'factotum' in every sense of the word. He had been with him during the last part of his time at Steglitz, and now accompanied his master to Frankfurt and became porter of the new

Institute. Then came a long, wide corridor with broad, high windows looking on to the street and laboratories on the other side. Two of the laboratories were Ehrlich's working rooms. On

State Institute for Experimental Therapy, Frankfurt am Main

the first and second floors were a number of laboratories for his assistants, a library, a reading-room, rooms for the cleaning of glassware, etc.

Professor Doenitz and Dr. Max Neisser, who had been working with Ehrlich at Steglitz, and his assistant Dr. Julius Morgenroth, all came with him to Frankfurt and worked under his direction in the new Institute with its ample supplies and facilities. The Institute was generally called the Serum Institute for the sake of shortening the name and because the State Control of sera, as in Steglitz, was part of the daily routine work.

For the journeys every day to and from his home, 62, Westendstrasse, a pleasant red-brick house with a little garden full of roses and an ivy-clad iron fence in front of it, Ehrlich always preferred to travel in a 'Droschke' or horse-cab. He liked to have the carriage waiting at the gate while he collected all the little things he needed, books, note-blocks, papers and—most important—cigar-box, and then, while driving at a gentle trot, he continued his work, reading and making notes. He was so absorbed that he hardly paid any attention to the interesting and at times beautiful view this drive offered, passing the little front gardens of the Westendstrasse, across the wide square in front of the railway station, the Bahnhofsplatz, then the bridge crossing the lower part of the Main, the Wilhelmsbrücke, with a splendid view of the old Frankfurt cathedral, and finally passing the Hippodrome riding-school and through the wide chestnut alley Wilhelmstrasse and the gardens and green places of the Sandhofstrasse. Nor did he pay attention when sometimes the cab-driver, passing the Institute, went on into the nearby 'Stadtwald', the widespread forest on the outskirts of the town. When Ehrlich finally noticed this 'extra-tour', he would make a sign to the driver to turn, without any remark. He knew that his faithful wife had plotted this 'conspiracy' against him, in order to let him have the benefit of at least a little fresh air.

All the Frankfurt cab-drivers knew and liked him, and he enjoyed talking to them and hearing about their lives and families. They were all glad when they were called upon to drive him. Ehrlich's interest in people was so great that he avoided trams and buses with their many passengers. Their appearance and the expressions on their faces would reveal to his psychologically trained eye too much of their personalities; and this would absorb so much of his thoughts in reflections on their probable futures that it would disturb his scientific meditations.

While he had been at the Steglitz Institute Ehrlich had worked out the fundamental principles of the famous 'Side-chain Theory', which gave a scientific explanation for the formation and action of antibodies in the blood. The first idea of this theory had really begun much earlier, and the experiments which led to its working out covered a period of about ten years. During the first years of his work at Frankfurt Ehrlich was still ardently engaged upon it.

It was just at this time, in November 1902, that I began to work for Paul Ehrlich as his secretary 'on approval'. This trial period was adopted by his special wish; for he declared that he could not tell whether he would get accustomed to dictating his thoughts, letters and scientific papers. Later I learned the true reason. Once, in Berlin, Ehrlich had engaged someone to help him with his writing, but the typist wrote down all his inter-jections and repetitions, which produced a strange sort of script. Finally, becoming nervous because of his absent-minded way of working, she was unable to take down his dictation and ran away. Ehrlich wanted therefore to protect himself against a repetition of this experience.

To begin with, we made arrangements for three hours' work daily, but soon there was so much to be done that the time stipulated was not nearly sufficient. Later, when he was working on Chemotherapy, it became necessary to work almost day and night in order to keep up with the enormously increased amount of paper work. During this period, after innumerable experi-ments on animals, he worked out 606. Then followed more than a year of carefully and conscientiously carried out clinical experiments on patients, until finally the specific 606 could be released for the treatment of all syphilitic patients. About this, and the work involved, I shall say more later.

I regard it as a great and most happy episode in my life, that I was allowed to work for Ehrlich as his secretary day by day for thirteen years; and that, observing his actions, hearing him speak to his friends and colleagues, I was given an insight into the wonderful riches and greatness of his soul. Perhaps I shall be able here to give a fuller description of Ehrlich, the man and his work, than was possible in my first small book, 'Paul Ehrlich als Mensch und Arbeiter' (Deutsche Verlagsanstalt, Stuttgart, 1924). The task of drawing a biographical picture, faultless in detail, of every aspect of this genius is more than one person could hope to accomplish. However, from all the little events and characteristic features that I can collect together, a living portrait may be reflected, as in a mirror, not only of a great scientific investigator and discoverer but also of a beautiful and simple human soul.

.   .   .   .   .

Ehrlich's characteristic kindliness was conspicuously shown in his daily dealings with the people around him, especially in his fatherly attitude to his factotum, Kadereit. Every morning Kadereit brought the letters and other mail to Ehrlich's house. Then he had to open the letters and wait while his master read them as he ate a little of his breakfast, which was probably already cold. When Ehrlich made any remarks about the contents of a letter, Kadereit would reply and give his opinion in his dry matter-of-fact way. Then Kadereit had to put the mail and other things back into the big leather portfolio, and hurry back to the Institute to take "press-copies" of note-cards, called 'blocks' by Ehrlich, and distribute them to the persons to whom they were addressed, before Ehrlich himself arrived. In this way everyone at the Institute knew at an early hour each day what Ehrlich wished him to do. The 'blocks' were thin cards, 4 in. $\times$ $6\frac{1}{2}$ in. and $2\frac{1}{2}$ in. $\times$ 4 in., in various colours and bearing serial numbers, on which he wrote, day by day, notes and instructions for his collaborators and assistants, and even for himself. Heaps of 'blocks' had always to be ready at hand for him on his working table in his study at home as well as on his desk at the Institute.

Back at the Institute, Kadereit had to prepare all the laboratory items for Ehrlich's experiments; fill the bottles with different acids for the solution of dyes; put clean test tubes on the laboratory table; sort letters and copies of the answers in his own porter's room; sharpen a lot of coloured pencils; send off telegrams; give and take telephone messages; and perform many other miscellaneous duties. Ehrlich needed him all day long, and over and over again his call could be heard through the long corridor of the Institute: 'Ka—de—reit!' Kadereit knew that his master would not listen to any complaint about him and would always take his part. He was very dignified, loyal and discreet, and Ehrlich knew it. When his master was called to Berlin for an official conference at the Ministry, or for any other reason, all the efforts of the Institute staff to get some

information about it from Kadereit were in vain. When he did
see fit to speak of things that were going on, he always said:
'*we* have', '*we* do', 'this and that has happened to *us*.' He liked
to speak about the time when '*we* came from Berlin to Frankfurt', and, later, 'when *we* found 606.'

Kadereit was very proud when he had to accompany Ehrlich
to the railway station; and if there was time before the train
left—and there always was time, because Ehrlich did not like
hurrying to catch a train—he loved to sit beside him at a table
in the waiting-room, taking a glass of genuine Munich beer and
chatting to while the time away. He never forgot his position
towards Ehrlich, but in the privacy of his own room Kadereit
liked to speak of him as the 'father' to whom he was devoted
from the depth of his heart, and for whom he would go through
fire and water. Whenever I told him that Ehrlich's tie or some
other little item of dress was not quite in its place, he would
answer good-naturedly, in his Berlin dialect:

'Na, da wer'n wir man den Vater jleich wieder in Ordnung
bringen.' (Well then, we shall put father right at once.)

.   .   .   .   .

It may interest the reader if I now describe some of the
incidents which took place during a typical working day. It
is a day in 1903. I had then been working for him for some
months.

In his study, as in his reading-room at the Institute, everything is full and covered with manuscripts, periodicals and
books. Bookshelves rise from floor to ceiling, but the gigantic
table in the middle of the large room, the writing-desk at the
window, and every chair and armchair is piled with books and
papers. Even on the floor there are heaps, so much so that
between these and the table and other furniture only a narrow
'footpath' remains on which to walk. As Ehrlich never will take
his breakfast anywhere but in his study, and there is never a
place on which to put it, a very small square table is set up
beside the big table in the middle of the study. There he reads
his letters and, always smoking one of his big Havanas, writes
his first notes of the day. The breakfast he may forget to eat, but
cigars and mineral water must always be there.

From his bedroom adjoining his study a song can be heard.

THE FRANKFURT 'SERUM-INSTITUTE'

Ehrlich is singing 'Am grünen Strand der Spree' (On the green banks of the Spree). He likes to sing, but he sings out of tune.

A maid is busy dusting, but she is not allowed to touch or move any of the piles of books and other things.

As Ehrlich comes in from his bedroom, still humming to himself 'On the green banks of the Spree', one can see through the half-open door into the thick cigar-smoke. He is fully dressed, ready to go to the Institute—as he always was in the mornings—and carries his cigar-box, manuscripts and 'blocks' under his left arm, muttering to himself: 'Dieser faule Kopf (he's a bad lot) . . . *caput pigerrimum*!' referring with this insulting remark to one of his scientific opponents. To the maid, who is just about to leave the room, he says with an air of great importance:

'Tag ook!' Then, raising his right hand to warn her: 'Attention . . . attention . . . don't move anything . . . don't re-arrange anything . . . it is *dangerous*! Only I myself can do that.' Mysteriously he continues: 'Wissen Sie . . . verstehen Sie . . . (you know . . . you understand) I put poison between the books!'

The woman, frightened, replies:

'Oh, my goodness!'

Still keeping up the ominous tone he has assumed, Ehrlich goes on:

'Yes, and whoever moves some of the things . . . can *die*!'

The woman, realising that it is not quite so serious as all that, takes courage and answers:

'But *you* are doing it . . .'

'Yes, but that is something quite different. . . . I cannot be poisoned, because I have,' he continues in an undertone, 'taken the *antidote* . . . the poison will not hurt me!'

There is a knock at the door and at Ehrlich's 'come in', Kadereit enters bringing the mail. The maid, taking advantage of the opportunity, quickly leaves the room. Kadereit says, full of dignity:

'Morning, Herr Jeheimrat!'

'Tag ook . . . was gibts Neues?' (what is the news?)

Kadereit takes out of the portfolio a number of letters and periodicals, opens the letters and hands them, one by one, to Ehrlich, saying:

'Many letters, Herr Jeheimrat!'

He cuts open another letter, and as Ehrlich has not yet finished reading the previous ones, he looks at what is written in it. Then, passing it to Ehrlich, he remarks:

'Arrhenius is coming.'

Ehrlich, not really paying attention, says absent-mindedly:

'Yes, yes, . . . wieso denn . . . wieso denn?'

'Na, Arrhenius . . . from Stockholm.' By this brief description Kadereit means the famous Swedish investigator and great mathematician Professor Svante Arrhenius. Now all attention, Ehrlich takes the letter, evidently very pleased, reads it, and then exclaims joyfully:

'What? Arrhenius? Grossartig!' (Magnificent!)

Ehrlich and Arrhenius did not always fully agree with each other. About 1904 there was an angry scientific controversy between them, ending in Ehrlich's favour. But from that time onwards they were the best of friends.

After having given his master all the letters, Kadereit goes to the door and calls out:

'Dora! the breakfast!' and Dora, the maid, comes in at once. Ehrlich, having finished reading his letters, begins to write his 'blocks'. Dora puts the little tray with the breakfast in front of Ehrlich on the small table and pours out a cup of coffee for him. Ehrlich has to move his work a little to make room for the tray, and there is just a small space left for him on the little table beside the tray. Without looking up from his work, he nods to Dora, thanking her, and continues to write undisturbed while Kadereit stands beside him. Still writing, he says simply:

'Cigars . . .' Kadereit passes him the cigar-box, and with one hasty glance Ehrlich picks out a cigar, takes off the label, and cuts away a large piece on both sides—more than a third. Kadereit strikes a light for him.

Ehrlich smokes hastily, occasionally taking some water and continues to write. Kadereit reminds him:

'The breakfast, Herr Jeheimrat . . . the egg and the coffee, it is all getting cold!'

Just then the new housemaid comes in, bringing on a little tray a few letters that have come to the house. Not yet used to her new surroundings and the narrow passages in the study, her foot catches round a leg of the small table, she stumbles, and over goes the table with the breakfast and all the things upon it. The coffee is running over Ehrlich's coat, the egg lies broken on the floor, the china smashed on top of it, and among all this debris the written 'blocks'. Ehrlich has not yet touched the breakfast at all. The girl, with a terrified face, screams out: 'Jesus!' and rushes frantically out of the room.

Ehrlich gets up and says quite calmly:

'Now she has run away—the stupid goose—instead of clearing up the mess!'

Kadereit has already run after her and brings her back; and while the girl, red-faced and sobbing, picks up the broken pieces, Kadereit wipes the coffee off Ehrlich's coat with his big handkerchief which is red with large white spots. Then he helps the girl with her clearing up, and pushes her hurriedly towards the door.

At that moment the other door which leads to the study from Frau Ehrlich's sitting-room opens. She looks in, asking: 'What is going on, Paul?'

Kadereit has posted himself in front of the girl in such a way that Frau Ehrlich cannot see her, and she just has time to slip out of the door.

Ehrlich smiles at his wife, nods and says gently:

'Oh, nothing, nothing . . .' upon which Frau Ehrlich, not noticing anything, only remarks, as she retires to her room again:

'But there was some noise, I'm sure.'

Meanwhile Kadereit has put all the letters, writings, etc., into the big portfolio, and finally leaves the room, to return to the Institute.

After Kadereit has gone, Ehrlich remains a little while, standing there deep in thought. His mind is far away, occupied with his work, his problems. Then he opens the door into the hall and calls out:

'Dora—a horse!' referring to the horse-drawn cab which takes him every morning to the Institute, and is already waiting at the gate. Männe, the light-brown dachshund is waiting too, ready to jump into the cab as soon as he sees his master coming out of the house carrying under his arm his cigar-box and an envelope of enormous size containing manuscripts and documents. On this envelope is written, in very large characters by Ehrlich himself, the following:—

Prof.
Ehrlich
Frankfurt a/M.
Westendstrasse
62
Finder erhält (receives)
10 Mark.

Ehrlich puts all his things in the carriage beside him and continues to write his notes during the drive. Männe sits at his feet.

Having arrived at the Institute, Ehrlich gets out, the cigarbox under his arm, but the big envelope and its contents are absent-mindedly forgotten. Männe, the dog, stands waiting while Ehrlich pays the driver and touches the brim of his hat to him in a friendly parting gesture.

In the Serum Institute there is already much busy coming and going in the long corridors and the laboratories. Laboratory boys in large blue aprons are dragging big glass jars, about nineteen inches high and containing white mice, through the corridors. One of the boys drops a jar, which smashes to pieces on the stone floor. The mice run away, and the boy dashes after them, trying to recapture them, but with little success. Then Goeldner, who works in the laboratory for State Control of the sera, and has charge of the boys, appears. He looks at the boy and the escaping mice and rebukes him sternly:

'Now what have you been up to? Mind you catch all those mice again—or else!' and with a threatening gesture he goes down the steps out of the building. The boy, with a burning face, goes on chasing the mice, catches some of them and puts them in his apron.

Assistants are walking up and down the corridor, paying no attention to the boy, among them Dr. Morgenroth and Dr. Sachs, engaged in an animated conversation. They are discussing some scientific question, and now and then they say quite seriously, without moving a muscle of their faces: 'Wissen Sie—verstehen Sie' (you know, you understand). At first they used to repeat Ehrlich's characteristic interjections rather mockingly, but now they have caught the habit themselves. Finally they go into one of the laboratories on the right.

. . . . .

Now Ehrlich is coming up the steps, his dog Männe at his side. As he passes the door of Kadereit's room he calls out, without turning his head:

'Ka—de—reit! Mineral water!' and disappears into his laboratory.

At once Kadereit comes out, a jug with mineral water in one hand, a glass in the other, and runs after Ehrlich.

Ehrlich's laboratory at the Institute was narrow and extremely simple, with a single curtainless window opposite the door, looking out on to a small lawn surrounded by bushes and some red hawthorn and pine-trees. Behind these were the houses for the mice, rabbits and other animals, and in the background the large buildings of the City Hospital. In the middle of both side walls of Ehrlich's room doors led to other laboratories: to the left, into the section for State Control of the sera, and to the right, into Ehrlich's private laboratory. The space on the left wall towards the window was occupied by a sofa, a small cabinet with a sliding door for papers, on top of which a jug of mineral water and a glass were always ready for use, and next to this in the corner of the room a little table. In the niche under the window was a low bookstand filled with copies of printed articles. On the opposite side, in the corner next the window, was Ehrlich's desk, and beside it were some large bookshelves and a small bookcase. By the desk was Ehrlich's plain oak chair. Two other smaller chairs had to be placed close in front of the bookshelves, as otherwise there would not be enough room between the bookshelves on the one side and the sofa on the other.

It was evident that no one ever sat on the sofa, except perhaps in the very earliest days of the Institute. Later on it was obviously destined to bear only the heavy burden of the high piles of books placed upon it. The whole seat was covered with heaps of books, periodicals, documents and writings, some in large envelopes, others in large blue cardboard folders. The top of the writing-desk, the little table in the opposite corner and the bookstand beneath the window had suffered the same fate, as had the two chairs in front of the bookshelves, and also these

themselves. Thus there was really only one seat in the whole
room—Ehrlich's own chair. During the first years at Frankfurt,
whenever a visit by one of the Berlin Ministry officials (the
superior Government Authorities) or any other important person was announced, the sofa had to be cleared for the occasion.
Kadereit used to put all the piles of books, manuscripts, etc.,
under the sofa, replacing them the next day in exactly the same

Ehrlich's Study

order. Later, however, the piles grew so high that this procedure
was no longer possible.

The large drawers and pigeon-holes in the desk were entirely
filled with old papers. Everything new had to be put on top of
the desk or on the sofa or other places, and for this reason the
drawers were only very seldom opened. This was very good for
the mice, who took advantage of it by building their nests there.
I shall have more to say about this later.

Ehrlich was a man of hasty temperament, and yet also infinitely kind. He could laugh like a child and get angry like a
child. For days, even for weeks, he took no notice when one of
the laboratory boys passed by without greeting him in the corridor. Perhaps the boy had often said 'good morning', and

Ehrlich, absent-minded, had not noticed it, so the boy thought it was not necessary. It often happened that Ehrlich did not reply to my greeting either, and then another time he would salute me with his good-natured 'Tag ook' every time I went into his room, perhaps more than ten times during the day. And whenever Ehrlich became aware that one of the boys was not polite, he would give him a lecture that he would never forget. In one of his rare outbreaks of temper he once flung a book after Kadereit, who had misunderstood him and done something wrong. On another occasion Kadereit saw him put on his coat one morning, then immediately take it off again and, cursing to himself under his breath, throw it on the floor and stamp on it like a wayward child.

An unexpected annoyance, a disregard of his orders, generally made Ehrlich exclaim angrily and vehemently: 'Unerhört . . . unerhört!' (unheard of . . . it's unbelievable) while in a passionate outburst he lifted both arms almost up to the shoulders, giving the upper part of his body a sudden jerk and moving his hands as though to clench his fists. Or he would take the revers of his coat in both hands and tug at them impatiently, his whole body shaking in the effort to restrain his wrath.

And then again—and this was the real man—Ehrlich was full of that thoughtfulness for others and delicacy of feeling of which the incident at breakfast offers a striking example.

But let us continue to watch Ehrlich as he prepares for his day's work at the Institute. Kadereit, who has followed him into his room and put the jug of mineral water and the glass in their place, now helps Ehrlich to take off his hat and coat and hangs them on a hook behind the door in the right wall. Ehrlich always wears plain suits, without elegance, but distinguished looking: not at all neglected, as is often incorrectly said in descriptions of him which exaggerate some little carelessness of no importance. He had so much personal charm, such innate gentility and real kindliness of heart, that slight irregularities in his dress did not count and were not even noticed. He never put on in Frankfurt the white overalls which medical men generally wear. Perhaps he once wore them during the time when he was an assistant at the Charité Hospital in Berlin. He always wore dark suits, stiff white collars, the edges of which had to be turned back, leaving the neck in front bare, as can be seen in all

F

his photographs. His neckties had a large knot, not tied by himself, but ready-made and fastened with a buckle at the back.

His thoughts were so exclusively concerned with his plans and
problems that he paid little attention to outward appearances.

He was perpetually at war with his shirt-cuffs—detached
white cuffs which were generally called 'Röllchen', and kept
together with cuff-links. On entering his working-room he immediately took off both cuffs, put them together one inside the
other and hung them on one of the big clothes hooks on the
wall, next to his overcoat, where they remained until he left
the Institute to go home, unless during the day an important
visitor came to see him. After the visitor had left him he sometimes forgot to take them off again, and then it was amusing to
see him struggle with these refractory objects. During his test
tube experiments, or while he was writing and signing letters,
they would always slide down to the tips of his fingers. Repeatedly, with saint-like patience, he pushed them back into the
sleeves of his coat, ten times, a hundred times—without thinking how simple and easy it would be to take them off. Sometimes he tried to improve matters by stretching both arms up
above his head and shaking them, thinking that the cuffs might
slide back by gravity, but always in vain. He found them very
convenient, however, for making notes, and accordingly would
write on them with his lead pencil, or even a coloured pencil.
When the cuffs were covered with notes, he would write—
much to the distress of his wife and the laundry-woman—on his
shirt-front as well.

While Kadereit is still busy with his master, a barrel-organ
begins to play behind the Institute, under Ehrlich's window.
The man with the organ comes once or twice every week, as in
the courtyard of the little Steglitz Institute. He plays parts of
operas like 'Carmen', of the operettas 'Fledermaus', 'Gipsy
Baron', 'Vogelhändler', and other songs and popular music.
He receives a good reward and is very pleased when Kadereit
says to him: 'Go on playing'.

Männe, the dog, runs after Kadereit when he leaves the room,
because he knows that he must stay in Kadereit's room until
Ehrlich returns home.

The music stimulates Ehrlich, and going into his laboratory
next to his reading-room he begins to bustle about with test

tubes and substances, heating his experimental mixtures over
the flame of a Bunsen burner. Soon some of his assistants come
in to ask their chief for detailed instructions about the experiments outlined on the 'blocks' which Kadereit brought with
him earlier in the morning.

Ehrlich's capacity for work was enormous, and as he was himself indefatigable he expected collaborators and employees to be
the same. Professor Felix Pinkus mentioned this characteristic
in his obituary written after Ehrlich's death[1] and all he said led
up to this:

'Often very impatient during his daily work, Ehrlich would
devote years of the most intensive work to solving a question to
his satisfaction if this were at all possible. His laboratory work
was free from all restrictions of orthodox procedure, so much so
that he often gave orders which were quite contrary to all rules
and customs; but even the most extraordinary methods, when
used in his experiments, would lead to the successful conclusions
he expected. He was unaccustomed to going ahead slowly in one
direction; and yet, in spite of this, even the most painstaking
work could not ever quite satisfy his demand for precision.'

His control of the experiments, as well as the way he conducted them, was very peculiar. His whole system was largely
based on those 'blocks' as he called them—cards in different
colours, light yellow, orange, rose, bright red and medium blue,
as already described, on which he wrote all his instructions for
chemical and biological experiments, also for experiments to be
made in the cancer-research department, and for letters and
articles which he wished to have written. In fact, he planned on
them the whole programme for the tasks of each day, and wrote
them all himself in the morning at home and again in the evening. He evidently had, in using the different colours, a special
system of his own which simplified his control. On the 'blocks'
on which he wrote instructions for himself, he liked to put some
names, indications and clues or catchwords, all with one or more
exclamation marks, one or two huge full-stops as large as a half-
penny and a question mark. Then he would underline them or
draw a round or square frame around them, the whole being
written with a coloured pencil of a different colour from that of
the card itself. Only he knew the key to all these symbols. In

[1] *Medizinische Klinik*, 1915, No. 50/51.

using the coloured pencils he enjoyed a certain extravagance. He had hundreds of them—mostly blue and red, but in other colours also—always ready for use, in all the pockets of his coats and waistcoats, on his desk, and in all the drawers both at home and at the Institute. They had to be cut especially for his use, not longer than two to three inches, for he held them in a peculiar manner, inside the hollow of his hand, so that they had to be just the right length to fit. Once, when he was away in Berlin, his wife had his suits and his study at home put in order, and on this occasion whole piles of coloured pencils were discovered.

CHAPTER VII

THE 'SIDE-CHAIN' THEORY

SUDDENLY during this day which we have been watching there was some excitement at the Institute. Kadereit came in to Ehrlich's rooms, and as he opened the door and entered the study he called out to his master who was working in the laboratory:

'Herr Jeheimrat—a telegram!'

Ehrlich came, opened it and said:

'Good heavens! Krüss is coming!' Then, pointing to the sofa and the desk, he went on: 'Tidy up here—quickly.'

Kadereit began at once to put the books and piles of other things *underneath* the sofa, at which Ehrlich added, as he opened the door leading to the State Control 'Serum-Section':

'But put them in the right order, mind!' to which Kadereit replied:

'Jawoll, certainly Herr Jeheimrat.'

Having freed the sofa entirely, Kadereit tidied the piles on the desk and cleared one of the chairs. He went to the window and waved his hand towards the courtyard outside, upon which the music from the barrel-organ suddenly ceased in the middle of a song.

In the laboratory of the Serum-Section next door Ehrlich was announcing:

'Dr. Krüss will be here presently, Herr Kollege'.

Dr. Marx, an Army surgeon who was in charge of the section, replied:

'Oh, already?' and the voice of Goeldner could be heard calling out to the boys:

'Quickly now . . . tidy up . . . look snappy!'

Kadereit had meanwhile taken down the cuffs from the peg and handed them to Ehrlich, who put them back into his sleeves, nodding and saying:

'Tell Dr. Neisser and Dr. Sachs.'

Then Ehrlich began to rummage among the contents of a little shelf above his desk, to the left, where he kept all sorts of

65

precious things in old cigar-boxes; tiny glasses with special chemical preparations, etc., and next to them small bottles of dyes. He took down some of the latter and read the labels, took a handful of coloured pencils out of his pocket, chose one and put the others back, pulled out the left cuff from his coat-sleeve and wrote something on it in red pencil—a note for a special requirement. He was always so deeply engaged in his experiment that his thoughts could not be disturbed or distracted by any outside happening, not even by the visit of a representative of the Ministry.

Kadereit ushered the visitor in: Dr. Krüss, representative of the Berlin Government. Immediately afterwards Dr. Marx came in from the Serum-Section, and Dr. Neisser and Dr. Sachs from the corridor.

After formal greetings had been exchanged, Ehrlich offered his cigars. Dr. Neisser and Dr. Marx were a little taller and broader than Ehrlich. Professor Krüss and Dr. Sachs were both very tall. Dr. Neisser took a cigar and put it in the breast-pocket of his overall. The others began to smoke. As Ehrlich took the band off his cigar and cut *both ends*, he looked inquiringly at Dr. Neisser and said:

'Herr Kollege Neisser?' to which the other replied with a frank laugh:

'It is too strong for me. . . . I must smoke it at home.'

They all laughed, smoked comfortably and contemplated their Havanas with much pleasure. Finally, Dr. Krüss turned to Ehrlich and remarked:

'Your recent article on the "Side-Chain Theory" is really extremely interesting, my dear Herr Geheimrat.'

'Do you think so . . . do you think so?'

'Yes, but'—and he gave a slightly embarrassed smile—'it is not so easy to understand.'

Ehrlich was astonished and asked:

'Ja, wieso denn . . . wieso denn? But it is quite simple, is it not, Herr Kollege Neisser?'

He looked at the others also, one after the other. They were thoughtfully inhaling the smoke of their cigars, with a faint, hardly noticeable affirmative movement of their heads. Dr. Sachs said:

'Wonderful—this cigar!' and they all laughed.

Ehrlich had taken out one of his coloured pencils from his pocket again, and lightly tapping the sleeve and front of Dr. Krüss's coat with the tip of it, he declared:

'Wissen Sie . . . verstehen Sie . . . my dear Dr. Krüss . . . I picture this to myself, thus: the cells have the ability to attract foreign chemical substances which have specific chemical relationship to the substances of the cell itself. Whenever such substances come in contact with the cell, a chemical binding takes place. This is as close, and as well adjusted, as a key is to its lock. *Re vera* . . . still another, better picture . . . wissen Sie, . . . verstehen Sie . . . In order to incorporate the chemical stuff, the cell will . . . so to speak . . . stretch out arms, "receptors", to catch and get hold of the substances. The group giving the foreign substance its affinity for the cell receptor, the haptophore group, will be caught by the receptor, the catching arm, and thus anchored to the cell protoplasm. If the foreign substance has also a toxophore group, giving it poisonous properties, the cell may be killed. If it survives, the receptors will be regenerated in excess, some will float off into the serum, and there function as a specific antibody for the foreign substance, having an affinity for it.'

Ehrlich explained all this in a very animated way, with lively movements, stretching out his arms and drawing them back, as though he were catching and pulling something towards himself.

Dr. Krüss was very interested and remarked, laughing:

'That sounds very nice and intelligible, but I still cannot altogether picture it quite clearly—not yet.'

To this Ehrlich replied:

'But it is very easy to demonstrate. I will make a drawing to show you . . . *eo ipso* . . .'

Ehrlich looked around for something to draw on. During his explanation he had been walking about, tapping Dr. Krüss and the others with his red pencil, scribbling figures on the door in passing, making scratches on the wall. But the coloured pencil was blunt, and the figures on the door and the wall were not clear. Then he had an idea. 'Ei—nen Au—gen—blick' (one moment), he said.

He went quickly into his laboratory and returned with a large piece of chalk.

'*Re vera*—I shall draw it *here*,' and he pointed to the floor. He had done this once before, for Robert Koch in Breslau at the very beginning of his 'Side-Chain Theory'. Ehrlich had been

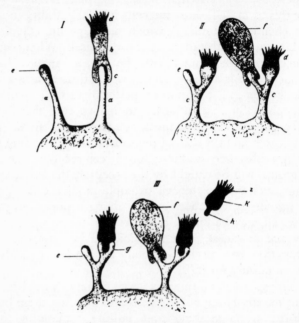

Diagram of Ehrlich's 'Side-Chain Theory' published in connection with the 'Anæmia' of Ehrlich and Lazarus in Nothnagel's 'Special Pathology and Therapy', Vol. 8, 1898–1901, as an appendix to Ehrlich's 'Schlussbetrachtungen', pages 163–185

Figure I. RECEPTOR OF FIRST ORDER. (*e*) haptophore complex; (*b*) adsorbed toxin molecule with (*c*) haptophore group; (*d*) toxophore group

Figure II. RECEPTOR OF SECOND ORDER with (*e*) haptophore group; (*d*) zymophore group and (*f*) adsorbed nutritive molecule

Figure III. RECEPTOR OF THIRD ORDER. (*e*) haptophore; (*g*) complementophile group; (*k*) complement with (*h*) haptophore; (*z*) zymotoxic group; (*f*) nutritive molecule

explaining his theories to Koch and his colleagues in a vigorous and lively manner, but Koch had stopped him saying:

'But, my dear colleague, in *this* way I cannot follow you, you must explain it a little more intelligibly.'

To this Ehrlich had quickly replied:

'Gewiss, das werden wir gleich haben' (Certainly, we shall get there at once), and had suddenly drawn in chalk on the floor a diagrammatic description of his scientific ideas.

So on this occasion Ehrlich stooped and again began to draw on the floor a plan of his 'Side-Chain Theory' with chalk. As there was not enough room, he turned back the edges of the brightly coloured carpet in front of the sofa in order to gain more space. The three men, Dr. Krüss, Dr. Neisser and Dr. Sachs watched the demonstration attentively, nodding their heads, and Dr. Krüss said:

'That is plausible, now I can understand.'

Enthusiastically, waving his arms about with the long-dead cigar in one hand and the chalk in the other, Ehrlich continued to explain:

'Whenever there is infection, and reaction in defence of the cell has set in through the production of antitoxin, this antitoxin will, *re vera*, because it has a specific relationship to the toxin, be anchored to it right there.'

His three listeners nodded approvingly, and Ehrlich beamed with delight.

Ehrlich had once written to his friend Professor Christian Herter of New York that he had a special ability to see pictorially all the ideas and problems he had in mind: the benzene ring, the chemical formulae, the side-chains, receptors, complements, etc. About all these ideas and plans he could talk, go on talking, talk incessantly, enthusiastically, convincingly, while in common every-day matters he was laconic, using short, telegram-like phrases. To explain his theories he gave vivid word-pictures, drew an exact parallel, in his ardent desire that those who listened to him could see, as he was able to see. Therefore he would show his great delight and happiness when he saw that he was understood.

Dr. Krüss then remarked with an amused laugh:

'Such an instructive demonstration ought to convince even your most obstinate opponent.'

At this Dr. Neisser and Dr. Sachs joined in the laughter, and Ehrlich said with energy:

'You mean Dr. Gruber, that faulen Kopp (bad lot)—*caput pigerrimum*!'

'It is really incredible that he should nickname you "Doctor

Fantasy", and it shows very bad taste on his part,' said Dr.
Krüss indignantly.

Ehrlich repeated excitedly:

'Ja, unerhört . . . unerhört! (incredible, incredible) wissen
Sie . . . verstehen Sie?'

But while he was speaking, he was already thinking of something else, his thoughts had gone far ahead. He wanted to show
the Government representative the experiments on cancer,
which were carried out by Dr. Sticker in a laboratory on the
second floor. As he suggested this he was already opening the
door leading to the corridor and going out in front of the others.
He never concerned himself in the least with questions of
etiquette and would rush in and out in front of even the most
important visitors. Though naturally courteous in word and
action towards everyone, he paid little attention to formal rules
of procedure. For this reason, on a visit he paid to English
scientific friends, one of them remarked, smiling at his peculiarities: 'You are no courtier'. But no one ever blamed him for
it, everyone loved and admired him, he found friends everywhere. A colleague from abroad once remarked to his friend
Professor Kossel of Heidelberg:

'Ehrlich is a man whom one can love as a child is loved.'

Meanwhile, I was sitting at my typewriter in a small, light
room filled with bookcases, next to the big library on the second
floor. I was soon interrupted by the assistant, Dr. Morgenroth,
who came in saying:

'Good morning, Fräulein Marquardt. Can I dictate to you
the article for the Chief?'

'Yes, of course, Dr. Morgenroth. Shall we do it in the
library?'

Dr. Morgenroth nodded: 'Please', and opened the door into
the next room, the library. This was at the back of the Institute,
and had two large windows with a fine view of the trees in the
garden, the buildings of the City Hospital, and far away the
Taunus Mountains.

Walking up and down, Dr. Morgenroth began:

'It is not easy, and not without danger, to form a sound
criticism of a wide field of work, accessible to experimental investigation, on the basis of purely literary studies. Nor is it easy

to analyse the material which is difficult for outsiders to comprehend! . . . Have you got that?'

I nodded: 'Yes.'

'And what comes now?'

'Now comes Dr. Fantasy—Dr. Gruber—der faule Kopp.'

The reply was a roar of laughter. 'Right! Well then: "All the more surprising is it that Dr. Gruber has just chosen as the basis of his attack the field of the toxins, which he himself admits he knows only from the study of the literature on the subject. Faced by such a critic I find myself in the disagreeable position of a man who is supposed to discuss colours with a colour-blind person." '

From outside came the faint sound of Ehrlich's voice downstairs calling out: 'Ka—de—reit! Mar—kart!'

'I must go down. Excuse me,' I said as I left the room.

'We will continue to-morrow,' said Dr. Morgenroth.

. . . . .

Entering Ehrlich's study I said: 'Good morning, Herr Geheimrat,' and took up my position at the writing-desk where there was a small space just large enough for my note-book.

'Tag ook,' said Ehrlich. 'Well now, we shall write: "Dear friend, I shall be glad to see you in Berlin. They are shooting into my antitoxin-tower—but I have a strong answer for them. When you come with me to Frankfurt I shall show you my experiments".'

Dr. Morgenroth, still laughing, came in and said something to Ehrlich in an undertone, of which I could catch the words 'Gruber' and 'Fauler Kopp'. Ehrlich burst out laughing, like a child.

'Mar—vel—lous! Ex—cel—lent!'

Still laughing he turned again to me:

'Al-so, what did I say?'

'Nothing as yet, Herr Geheimrat. The other letter was finished,' I replied a little nervously.

'Al-so . . . Wissen Sie, verstehen Sie. . . . Ha! Ha ha! Ausgezeichnet (excellent), wunderbar! (marvellous)! A—l—s—o . . . "The necessity—eo ipso—arises of performing tests based on colour reactions not only on normal but also on pathological conditions. Two reactions seem to be suitable for such use in medicine, the diazo-reaction and a new one, the dimethylamidobenzaldehyde-reaction, which has not yet been published, and which gives with all urines, without exception, a marked and distinct reaction".'

I had stopped writing and looked up at Ehrlich.

'Ah, you did not get that, did you?' he said. 'One moment,' and he took the note-book which I had handed to him and putting it on top of one of the piles of books he wrote something in it and gave the notes back to me.

Ehrlich was smoking while he dictated, and a long cone of ash formed at the end of his cigar. This at last fell down, scattering ashes over Ehrlich's coat, but he did not notice. Nor had he remembered to take off his cuffs again after Dr. Krüss had gone, and these were now a perpetual nuisance to him. They kept sliding out of his sleeves as a result of his lively gestures while he was speaking and dictating and writing in my note-book. Several times he stretched up first one arm and then the other, shaking it to make the cuff slide back into his sleeve, but without any success. His tie became a little crooked through this effort, and part of it showed above the collar of his coat at the back where it was buckled. Such minor details made his dress appear a little careless, but it was never ridiculous as has sometimes been incorrectly alleged.

Without a break Ehrlich resumed his dictation:

' "The shade varies, in accordance with the intensity of the reaction. In some cases there is only a slight change, in others the urine is coloured bright red. That must still be worked out further." Thank you very much,' he said, nodding slightly.

I got up to go. Ehrlich had already gone to the door, opened it and called out: 'Kadereit! Cigars!'

Kadereit's door opened and closed and he came running. I left the room somewhat puzzled. In the corridor I was followed by Dr. Morgenroth, who had just come from the Serum-Section. He said, laughing:

'I'm sure you did not write down all that "parenthetic" stuff, Fräulein Marquardt—wissen Sie, verstehen Sie.'

'No,' I replied hesitantly, and then went quickly into Kadereit's room.

Ehrlich's only real passions were for cigars and books. For his imported Havanas he had a regular supplier in Frankfurt, and for occasional orders there was also another cigar shop in Frank-

furt and one in Berlin. He was always informed of the arrival of
the different kinds he preferred. Then the cigars he ordered
were stored by the cigar firm to be looked after properly and
sent to him as required. Every day at least once, often twice, a
box containing twenty-five of these big cigars had to be delivered; and if the delivery was just one quarter of an hour late
the telephone would ring and keep on ringing until the errand
boy arrived on his bicycle carrying the precious order. Ehrlich
needed 'strong stimulants', as he himself called them, and how
strong they were was made evident by the fact that all his
friends and colleagues knew and appreciated their value, but
they often feared their strength by which an ordinary smoker
would probably be upset. Ehrlich, however, smoked them
incessantly, from morning till night.

Kadereit was speaking at the telephone when I entered his
room.

'Is that Wetzlar? Please send a box of cigars—yes, as always—
but quickly—send immediately,' and he laughed, 'send a
mounted messenger—on his bicycle!'

When Kadereit turned and saw me standing there, puzzling
over my notes and chewing my pencil, he asked sympathetically:

'Well, how are you getting on?'

'Oh,' I answered timidly, 'Herr Geheimrat has written here
into my notes a word that I did not understand, and now I
cannot read it, and I did not dare ask Dr. Morgenroth to tell
me. Can _you_ read this?'

I showed him the word. Kadereit put on his spectacles,
assuming an air of importance, and looked at my notes:

'No, I've not heard that before—must be something new
again—that happens every day.'

'What did Dr. Morgenroth mean by saying it was to be hoped
I had not written all that "parenthetic" stuff?'

'That "parenthetic stuff"? Oh yes, Herr Jeheimrat always
says "wissen Sie, verstehen Sie, also" (you know, you understand, well then) and such like.'

'I certainly did not write those,' I answered, laughing.

'That's all right then,' he said. And then he told me the story
of the secretary in Berlin who could not understand Ehrlich's
way of dictating and ran away in a panic.

'Oh, I see,' I answered slowly. 'That is the reason why Herr

Geheimrat said to me at the beginning that we should have to try first, and he did not know whether he could do it.'

As I went out I said:

'I shall go and see my doctor this afternoon and ask him about the word.' Turning back I added: 'And Kadereit, you

Standing from left to right: *Dr. Shiga; Wunsch (Staff); Dr. Noeggerath; Goeldner (Staff); unknown doctor; Kaul (Staff); Dr. Keyes; Kadereit; Dr. Sticker; Dr. Hans Sachs*

Seated: *Dr. Apolant; Dr. Julius Morgenroth; Ehrlich; Dr. Max Neisser; Dr. Embden; Dr. Lippstein*

had better go and look after Herr Geheimrat. Cigar ash has been falling on his coat, and his necktie . . .'

'Yes, yes,' said Kadereit quickly, 'I'll go at once and fix "father" up,' and he rushed out past me towards Ehrlich's room.

In the corridor Dr. Marx, the Army-surgeon working in the Serum Section, was standing speaking to Dr. Neisser. They came a few steps nearer, and as I went towards the stairs Dr. Marx said:

'You had better not count too much on your work here, Fräulein Marquardt. I do not believe there is going to be very much . . .'

'On the contrary, Herr Kollege,' interrupted Dr. Neisser, 'I believe there will be a great deal to do. The work, in my opinion, will grow to be very extensive indeed!'

And Dr. Neisser was right. How the work grew, we shall see later.

.   .   .   .   .

That afternoon I went to see my doctor, the Sanitätsrat (Health Councillor) in a little village in the Taunus Mountains near Frankfurt. Dr. Neuroth, a kindly man, with a little stumpy nose, a reddish face and large spectacles, asked good-naturedly:

'Well, what is wrong?'

'You know, I am now working for Professor Ehrlich. This morning in his dictation he said a word that I did not understand. Then he wrote it himself in my note-book—and then I could not read it.' I showed him my notes. 'Do *you* know what that could mean?'

Putting his spectacles straight, the Sanitätsrat took my notes, but he could not make out the writing. He picked up his magnifying glass and looked through it, then shook his head seriously.

'I cannot read it either. It must be something new that Dr. Ehrlich has discovered.'

He tried again with the magnifying glass and said:

' "Dimethyl" and "reaction" I can make out. Just wait a moment.'

He found on his desk the last number of the *Medizinische Woche*, turned the pages, and then said suddenly:

'Yes, here we are, look—a new urine-reaction which he just describes briefly—the "dimethylamidobenzaldehyde-reaction". Has he completed it now?'

'Not yet. He says it has still to be worked out.'

'Yes, he is one of the few investigators who offer much—and still have much more in reserve. Every one of his articles brings out something new.'

'He is always saying,' I remarked, 'work much and publish little, with the greatest precision in the experiments.'

'Well you know,' Dr. Neuroth laughed, 'his publications are

not exactly few! But he does a great deal more work than he publishes, I know. It is really tremendous what he accomplishes!'

I took my leave, and said:

'I am *so* glad you have found this. Thank you very much.'

'Well, any time . . . It will not be an easy job, will it?'

'No, not easy. But *so* wonderful and interesting.'

CHAPTER VIII

AN EVENING AT HOME

LET us now picture Ehrlich at home with his family again. It is late in the afternoon, and he has scarcely arrived home before he is seated at the little table which the girl knocked over in the morning in his study. Coloured 'blocks' lie by his side, partly written. He goes on working without a pause, his cigar-box and mineral water and glass next to him. He smokes, puffs away, and drinks water. The smoke rises and fills the whole room. There is a knock at the door. Without looking up, Ehrlich says: 'Come in.'

Dora, the maid, appears.

'This morning's cab-driver has come and brought a parcel.'

'Yes, all right, all right, a parcel? A-l-s-o, let him come in,' says Ehrlich, still continuing with his work.

Dora calls the cab-driver, who enters, very embarrassed, his hat in his hand, carrying the big envelope, marked: 'Prof. Ehrlich, Frankfurt a/M., Westendstrasse 62, Finder receives 10 Marks', which Ehrlich left behind in the cab in the ·morning. (In Steglitz also he had his Berlin address in the Lützowstrasse written on a big envelope containing his documents; but he never forgot it on his way there.)

'Good evening, Herr Professor,' says the driver.

Ehrlich looks up, his head leaning forward just a little, his spectacles on the point of his nose. He looks over the top of his glasses, and the deep wrinkles on his forehead deepen still more. This was a characteristic attitude whenever he was working, in study or laboratory. He replies:

'Tag ook. Also, what nice thing are you bringing me?'

'There is the parcel here which Dr. Ehrlich left this morning in my cab.'

'A-l-s-o, man'—Ehrlich laughs aloud—'that is really great . . . grossartig . . . ausgezeichnet!'

He takes the parcel and looks at the writing. The man stands waiting and says:

G

'I only found it after I had taken another gentleman in my cab, and then I was far away and could not come back at once.'

Ehrlich nods, very pleased, and having already taken money out of his pocket, he gives it to the man.

'Al—so . . . well then! there are the ten marks.'

Then he takes out another coin and adds:

'And, so that you may also have something for yourself,' and he hands the money to the man, 'take these two marks as well! Thank you very much!'

Ehrlich lifts his right hand in a customary salutation, and nods.

The cab-driver stands there nonplussed. He wants to say something, and opens his mouth, but as Ehrlich has already begun to work again, he only bows awkwardly and says:

'Thank you very much, Herr Professor,' and turns and goes out of the room.

Outside, he hesitates a moment at the door, his hat still in one hand, the two pieces of money in the other. He stares at them in embarrassment, shaking his head and murmuring as he goes down the stairs:

'Ten marks—and then two more!'

Dora, leading him to the door, asks in astonishment:

'What is the matter? Is anything wrong?'

'Oh no,' says the driver, and laughs. 'It's quite all right. But a reward—and then again a reward for the reward!'

After this Ehrlich works without interruption until dinner time in the evening. We now see him in his dining-room with his wife and his two daughters—Steffa, aged eighteen, and Marianne (whom he nicknamed 'Janneck') aged sixteen—at table.

Dinner, during which there has been much lively conversation about the events of the day, is over, and Dora is clearing the table and replacing the tablecloth with a large white oilcloth cover.

Ehrlich always ate very little at dinner. During the day, at the Institute, he ate nothing at all, merely smoking his incessant cigars and drinking mineral water. He ate a little something when he came home late in the afternoon, before he continued to work in his study or took a short nap, and for dinner he had little appetite. But he used to talk with his family, teasing them

all and being teased by his daughters about his 'enemies', the
'faulen Köpfe', Professor Gruber who called him 'Dr. Fantasy'
and others. This evening, as often, Ehrlich gets into a passion
and says excitedly:

'That man Gruber—*caput pigerrimum*—that incapable creature
—der ungeschickte Taperkerl—I'll show him!'

'You really should take that opposition a little less seriously,
Paul,' urges his wife. 'Pray do not get too excited in the discussion to-morrow at the Society for Internal Medicine!'

Ehrlich does not answer, but says to the girl Dora, who has
just finished arranging the table, 'Dora, the little game . . .'

So Dora gets a pack of cards from a drawer in the sideboard
and puts it on the table. Ehrlich shuffles them and begins to play
patience. Steadily puffing away at his cigar he shuffles the cards
with great care and ceremony, with the result that every few
weeks they become worn out and have to be replaced with new
ones. Finally he begins a game, with all sorts of mistakes and
deviations from the proper rules, but that does not trouble him
in the least.

Marianne remarks: 'Oh yes, Papa, you are going to Berlin
to-morrow. Will you bring back something nice for me?'

Ehrlich nods to her joyfully, looking over his spectacles.

'Yes, what is it that you would like to have as a nice present?'
Then, without waiting for an answer, he burst out laughing.
'Just think, children! Didn't I forget all about the large envelope with the notes on animal experiments with which I am
going to smite the enemy Gruber in the discussion to-morrow?
I left it in the cab this morning! Just imagine that!' He laughs
heartily and all the time goes on shuffling the cards.

His wife and daughters cry out simultaneously in alarm:

'For Heaven's sake, Papa!' and 'But Paul!'

'Oh Papa, what ever are you going to do now?'

'A—l—s—o' (well now), replies Ehrlich, still laughing,
'we-ell, you see, the cab-driver I had this morning just brought
it back to me.'

'But Papa, how did he know?'

Ehrlich goes on placing the cards, while the others watch
him, and smiling mischievously, he says:

'Now you can see how cautious your father is! Also, I had
written my address on the envelope—really very large, you

know'—and he makes a descriptive movement with his hand, holding the cards and nodding to it—'and I added that—well—*eo ipso*—the honest finder would be rewarded with ten marks.'

They all laugh. 'So you have—*re vera*—really paid the ten marks?'

'But of course, children, of course! Certainly I paid them.' Ehrlich laughs again. 'And as the cab-driver should have something for himself as well, I gave him also another two marks.'

His wife and daughters are at first stupefied, then they burst out laughing again.

'So you have paid the reward, and on top of it another *extra* reward!' says his wife reprovingly.

'Papa, you are charming!'

'Ja, wieso denn . . . wieso denn?' (But how is that, how is that?) Ehrlich cannot understand their amusement.

As his games of patience never come out properly, Ehrlich has meanwhile several times shuffled the cards and with the utmost serenity started afresh.

'Paul, what you are doing is all *wrong*!' says his wife, pointing to the cards. 'Never in your life will you make the game come out, you are not putting the cards right, not at all.'

'Right! That will never come out in my life-time.' He throws the cards down. 'Well now, what about a little music, my dear Hete?' And he moves his hands as if playing the piano.

'Oh yes, Mamma, please, please,' beg his daughters with enthusiasm.

Marianne takes her mother by the hand and pulls her along into the small parlour adjoining the dining-room. At first she is a little reluctant, shaking her head and murmuring with slight resistance that she is 'not in the mood to-day'. But Steffa, humming cheerfully to herself, has already gone to turn on the light, open the grand piano, put out the music and arrange the piano-stool. Then her mother and Marianne, followed by Ehrlich, come in.

Almost without exception, so Frau Ehrlich once told me, her husband asked her to play something every evening after dinner. He always asked her jokingly, in a variety of different ways. If, now and then, she did not feel like playing, there was great disappointment, and his face wore a sad expression. If, as usual, she complied with his wish, Ehrlich would walk up and down and to and fro, while she played waltzes or parts of operettas. The gayer the melodies, the more animated and full of joy he would be. He always said that his best ideas would come to him at these times. During the playing of a piece of solemn, serious music, he would grow silent and earnest. When one of his favourite pieces was played in due course he became animated again and would hum the music to himself.

There was, however, one evening each week when Frau Ehrlich was not asked to play the piano, for every Saturday a new number of a thirty-pfennig crime magazine arrived, the fascinating contents of which always broke off at the height of the excitement on the last page—to be continued. The reading of this weekly paper, with its cover showing the most lurid pictures of murder and crime, occupied the whole evening, and Ehrlich would not miss this 'distraction' for anything.

At one time another of his evening amusements was working out mathematical problems. In 1905 his younger daughter Marianne, who was by then eighteen, married Dr. Edmund Landau, Professor of Mathematics at the University of Goettingen; and Ehrlich had a regular correspondence with his son-in-law about these mathematical problems. Professor Landau has stated that his father-in-law never thought of working seriously at any of the modern branches of mathematics, not even at differential and integral calculus, but that he set himself quite complicated problems on combination in connection with the summation of unending series, without any relation to chemical or other questions of experimental science. In these the 'E' series[1] played a prominent part. His solutions were worked out quite empirically. By numerical calculations he contrived to guess at the existing general laws, and in almost every case his suppositions proved to be correct. Later, however, this kind of pastime was dropped.

Ehrlich was not specially interested in painting, and declared that his artistic taste and comprehension were 'at zero'. With regard to music this may also be said to be true, in view of his rather naïve preference for barrel-organ music. He never went to concerts or the opera, but sometimes he would enjoy a visit to a variety or dancing show. This would remind him of his

[1] 'E' Series = exponential series : $e = (1 + 1/n)^n$.

school-days in Silesia when he had organised dancing in the open air with other boys and their sisters.

On this particular evening, Frau Ehrlich begins with a waltz by Johann Strauss. Steffa turns the music for her, and Marianne, who has gone into the larger adjacent room, begins to dance and comes in dancing.

Ehrlich goes to and fro, beating time to the music. He looks very pleased, and when the music stops he pats Marianne's cheek and says:

'Nice, very, very nice!'

After this Frau Ehrlich plays Escamillo's song from Carmen, 'Into battle, Torrero'. Ehrlich is particularly fond of this song, and as Marianne hums it, beating time to the music, his cheerfulness is at its height.

All of a sudden he stands still, absorbed and wrapped in thought. As the playing ends he looks up with a bewildered expression as though his thoughts were coming back from far away, and says with a smile:

'Now you see, children, an entirely new idea has just come to me at this moment.'

Later in the evening after his wife and daughters have wished him good night, Ehrlich returns to the dining-room and goes on with his work. To the last remarks of his family before they retired he answered only 'ah!', 'yes' or 'really?' in an absent-minded way. His thoughts were already far away in the realm of his scientific work. He pushes the cards on the table out of the way and begins to work and smoke again. He writes on and on, the room becomes thick with cigar-smoke, and the hands of the big clock move on until well after midnight.

All the thoughts that came to him during his games of cards and the music later in the evening now take on a proper form. He writes numerous 'blocks' with notes for himself and instructions for his assistants. Ehrlich said himself that this was 'the most important part' of his working day, and he found that after ten o'clock in the evening, when all was quiet, was the best time for him to plot out the next day's work and write his instructions. He even wrote postcards to himself and sent them off, to remind him, when they returned by post, of something he must not forget. For a similar reason his watch-chain always had a thick knot in it. But the knot was never undone.

Ehrlich never forgot certain things, such as ordering a special kind of Christmas cake of which his daughters were very fond. This was a kind of wedding-cake which formerly in Germany was always seen at every big wedding party. It was called 'Baumkuchen' (tree-cake) and was made to perfection by certain famous cake manufacturers. The cake consisted of ten or more layers, getting smaller towards the top. It was covered with delicious icing, which hung down like icicles at the protruding edges of the layers, giving the cake the appearance of a snow-covered Christmas-tree. On the other hand, he regularly forgot the most important family dates and birthdays, of which he always had to be reminded.

Much has been said about Ehrlich's forgetfulness, and such practices as having his address written on the large envelope, with the words 'Finder will receive ten marks', seem to be a proof of this. Nevertheless, he was not forgetful in the strict sense of the word, but merely so preoccupied with his scientific problems that everyday matters had to remain in the background. He knew exactly where to find a certain chemical substance amongst all the innumerable little bottles and phials in his laboratory. He could find an important document or manuscript from among the piles on the old sofa, his writing-desk or the chairs stacked high with books and papers in his study. Nor was he ever at a loss to find in his library, or in the piles on the old sofa, the book in which he hid part of his quarterly salary—his favourite place for his 'savings'. One of these books was found to contain some hundreds of marks when, after his death, his books were temporarily taken to the Senckenberg Library in Frankfurt to be catalogued. But very often there were no 'savings' to hide, for as soon as he received his salary he had to spend it all in settling the alarmingly large bills for cigars and books.

At last, very late, Ehrlich retires, leaving the thick cigar-smoke behind him, but even in bed he often continues to read and write notes.

CHAPTER IX

'SIDE-CHAINS' AND 'MAGIC BULLETS'

THE next day Ehrlich set out for the station, accompanied by his faithful servant Kadereit, to go to Berlin to attend a meeting of the Society for Internal Medicine. Kadereit carried his travelling-rug, a small valise and his portfolio containing documents and manuscripts. Ehrlich had, as always, a cigar-box under his left arm. At the main Frankfurt station they went into the crowded waiting-room, for there was plenty of time before the train left. Seated at a small table they had a glass of beer and talked of all sorts of things, about Kadereit's wife, and about his daughter, who would soon be confirmed and leave school.

Then they went to the train for Berlin. Kadereit found a good seat for his master, arranged everything for him, wished him a pleasant journey and took his leave. Ehrlich nodded good-bye to him kindly, and then at once began to work, making notes on his 'blocks' with coloured pencils which he had already unpacked and placed ready to hand.

Another passenger entered the compartment and took the seat opposite, but Ehrlich did not look up and continued his writing. When he finally noticed the new-comer, he exclaimed with pleasure:

'Ah, my dear Count—where have *you* come from?'

It was a great landowner from Silesia where he was born, a well-known Member of Parliament whom Ehrlich had known for a long time.

'I have just come from Wiesbaden, where I had some business to attend to,' said the Count, 'and now I am going to Berlin. After that I shall go home. But how glad I am, dear Geheimrat, to meet you like this.'

Suddenly Ehrlich asked him, with a smile like a mischievous little boy:

'Tell me, dear Count, couldn't you, from your experience as a Member of Parliament, suggest to me some trick by which I could reduce an adversary—wissen Sie—verstehen Sie—to silence?'

The Count replied, laughing:

'It is very kind of you, dear Geheimrat, to ask my advice; but I am only an ordinary man, and understand very little about scientific matters. I should at least know what the question is about—*who* is it whom you want "to reduce to silence"?'

Ehrlich looked at him over his big, thick-rimmed spectacles, and the wrinkles on his forehead deepened:

'Wissen Sie, verstehen Sie (you know, you understand) there is this Geheimrat Gruber in Munich—*caput pigerrimum*—who attacks my side-chain theory. Yet he has—*re vera*—not made a single experiment himself, the incapable fellow! It would be very easy for him to do so, in accordance with my published reports, and indeed—*eo ipso*—he will have to if he wants to carry on a scientific argument!'

The Count nodded and laughed. 'Then it is he who must be slain?'

'I must explain to you,' replied Ehrlich quickly. 'According to my theory on the formation and action of antitoxins in the blood-serum and the importance of the side-chains. . . .'

'What are side-chains?' interrupted the Count.

'We-ell—you will see, dear Count—I will make a drawing to show you.'

He rummaged among his 'blocks' and tried to make a sketch, but the train was very shaky, and the coach in which they were travelling rocked to and fro so terribly that it was impossible. Undaunted, Ehrlich said: 'Just a second!' and crossing his left leg over his right knee he held his foot tightly to keep it steady, and proceeded to draw in red pencil the outlines of his side-chain theory on the sole of his shoe.

The Count looked on with much interest. 'Marvellous! And what now?' he said.

'Wissen Sie, verstehen Sie—this represents the cell in the organism. Here'—and he pointed to it with his red pencil—'the cell pushes forward arms which will catch and seize, and which I call "receptors" . . .'

'Tickets, please,' interrupted the Collector, who had come to punch the tickets. After he had left the compartment, Ehrlich continued his explanation, accompanying it with movements of his arms which he stretched out and drew back in turn:

'Now, if there is an infection in the organism, producing a toxin by which the living cells of the organism are attacked, the organism creates the corresponding antitoxin, to defend itself, by a process in which the "arms" or "receptors", with a specific affinity for the toxin, are produced in excess by the cells, to replace those with which the toxin first combined. You see, you understand, I have chosen this diagrammatic explanation of the manner in which immunisation takes place in the living organism, to show how the antitoxins are formed in the living body, by a process analogous to the excessive replacement with which the body tissues repair any kind of injury.'

'That all sounds very plausible.'

'Ja, natürlich, natürlich' (yes, naturally, naturally).

'And how is it that they doubt these explanations?' asked the Count.

'They *do not* doubt them,' said Ehrlich with growing passion, 'Arrhenius and Madsen, Sachs, Morgenroth, Wechsberg and Neisser and all the others have confirmed my detailed schemes —all except that Dr. Gruber in Munich—der faule Kopp—who calls me "Doctor Fantasy!" '

The Count burst out laughing and exclaimed: 'Excellent!' He thought it all a great joke.

Ehrlich paid no attention to this interruption and continued indignantly:

'He has the impudence to say that my "complements" are "wishes swimming in serum"!'

But the Count's laughter was infectious, and soon Ehrlich was laughing too and went on more mildly:

'He would have done better if he had made some of the very easy experiments himself instead of flinging his groundless assertions into the world—the incapable creature!'

The Count, still laughing, said:

'And you expected that I should be able to tell you how to dispose of this blockhead? I am sure that you yourself have much better weapons to hand', and he pointed to the notes on his animal experiments which Ehrlich had taken out of the big envelope. All through the conversation he had been tapping them, emphatically gesticulating, with his coloured pencil or his thick-rimmed spectacles which he kept on taking on and off. Ehrlich nodded.

'Yes, of course, animal experiments—whole series of animal experiments—wissen Sie—verstehen Sie,—*they* are proofs indeed!'

Meeting of the Society for Internal Medicine in Berlin

The hall where this meeting, for which Ehrlich had travelled to Berlin, was being held was full to overflowing. He was on the platform defending his theories from the attacks of Dr. Gruber, and won the support of the meeting. He ended his speech thus:

'To sum up: Dr. Gruber's statement that "Ehrlich's theory is mistaken and should disappear as quickly as possible from scientific circles" has not been successfully proved, rather the contrary. I almost wonder whether it was necessary for me to make this detailed reply to an attack so crude and strange that it might seem to confirm my ideas by its own peculiarity! But I have thought it my duty to conduct this same company of investigators along the entangled paths of Dr. Gruber, so that you should not be induced by an abundance of misunderstandings and misleading interpretations to discredit a promising field of medical research.'

Thunderous and prolonged applause greeted Ehrlich's speech. A great number of the members, among them famous investigators, came up to shake hands and congratulate him. Everyone at the meeting agreed that although 'little Ehrlich' was not a great orator, yet whenever he made a speech he always had something important to say, something of significance in medical research. He did not always keep to the point, and sometimes became embarrassed, taking off his spectacles and swinging them round in noticeable confusion before putting them on again. But they agreed that his pictorial explanations of his Side-chain Theory, his comparison with the lock and key, were excellent, and greatly facilitated the comprehension of events in the organism which are often difficult to understand. They knew that his investigations during the past ten years had greatly furthered the whole science of medicine, and that without his terminology, his reactions and staining experiments, one could not get along with all the new problems.

It may or may not have been on this occasion that Ehrlich took the night train back to Frankfurt from Berlin accompanied by his two friends from London, the well-known Professors of Pathology Sir Almroth E. Wright and William Bulloch. At any rate, it was after some Congress in Berlin, and it is very likely that it happened on this occasion. Professor Bulloch wrote to me at length about it as an example of Ehrlich's vehement way of speaking.

The three friends were in the night train from Berlin to

Sir Almroth Wright about 1904

Frankfurt. Even while they were getting into the train and finding seats, Ehrlich was talking animatedly and incessantly:

'A-l-s-o . . . I have at last pushed that man—that dunder-head—to the wall so that he is unable to squeak any more! Animal experiments, my friends, you see, you understand, long series of animal experiments—those are what count!'

To this his friends replied: 'Now your "Side-chain Theory" is safe and you can continue your work in peace.'

It may be mentioned here that Ehrlich liked to give his friends Latin nicknames. He referred to his friend Dr. Albert Neisser, the great Breslau Professor of Dermatology, as 'Albertus magnus'; Professor Ludwig Pfeiffer, his comrade at the University, was called 'Pifferaro'; A. von Wassermann was 'Aquaticus'. Abusive names, such as 'Fauler Kopp' (idle block-head), 'Ungeschickter Taperkerl' (one who does everything wrong) and *'Caput pigerrimum'* were also much used in his letters. There was one investigator to whom Ehrlich attributed the habit of coming forward, with claims to priority of observa-tion, whenever Ehrlich published some new results of his own and the conclusions which he based on them, saying that he had made the very same observations long before Ehrlich had done so. This man was indignantly referred to by Ehrlich in letters to his friends as 'den grössten Neidhammel der Welt, dem er unbedingt eins auf den Hut geben muss!' (the most jealous beast [literally: the greatest envy-sheep] in the world, who must certainly have his hat bashed in); 'Hut' being used, of course, in reference to the last syllable of his name which ended in 'huth'.

When, on this train journey to Frankfurt therefore, his friends asked Ehrlich: 'What are your future plans now?' his gay and lively manner left him suddenly, and he replied with a frown:

'Also . . . wissen Sie, verstehen Sie, it seems that Aquaticus means to play me a nasty trick! Pifferaro told me before the lecture that Aquaticus is making experiments with a certain dye with which *I* am working!' Then he called out angrily at the top of his voice: 'Das ist ein unverschämter *Dachs*! (He is an impudent Badger!) Meddling in my experiments and making a mess of it! How the dickens did he get the dye? It is not to be had in any chemists or anywhere else!' Then still more loudly he called out furiously: 'An impudent badger—that's what he is!'

Then the guard on the train came in and said:

'The other passengers want to sleep, and ask if you will be quiet, please.'

'Oh!' said Ehrlich somewhat indignantly, and was quiet and sulky for a moment. Then suddenly he whispered to Professor Bulloch:

'But my dear friend—this fellow *is* an impudent badger!' and his voice rose until he repeated: 'An impudent badger!' at the top of his voice again.

Professor Bulloch and Sir Almroth Wright laughed heartily and tried to calm Ehrlich by saying 'ssh . . . ssh!' Of course,

the guard came back to complain again and said with an angry
threatening face:

'If the gentlemen do not keep quiet I shall have to ask all
three of them to leave the train!'

Evidently he thought that they were quarrelling with one
another. This threat did not impress Ehrlich in the least, and

Dr. William Bulloch about 1904

when the guard had left the compartment he repeated once
more, like a wilful stubborn child:

'But he *is* an impudent badger!'

At last he calmed down, but there was no sleep for anyone
that night. Instead he developed and explained to his friends
his plans for the immediate future. This he did in the animated
brisk manner so peculiar to him:

'Well—*eo ipso*—in my study of immunity, it has occurred to
me that by systematic and extensive chemical and biological
experiments it should be possible to find artificial substances

which are really and specifically curative for certain diseases, not merely palliatives acting favourably on one or another symptom such as fever, neuralgia, sleeplessness. . . . Such curative substances—*a priori*—must directly destroy the microbes provoking the disease; not by an "action from distance", but only when the chemical compound is fixed by the parasites. The parasites can only be killed if the chemical remedy has a particular relation, a specific affinity for them—if, in short, it is parasitotropic. This is a very difficult task, because it will be necessary to find chemical compounds which have a strong destructive effect upon the parasites, but which do not at all, or only to a minimum extent, attack or damage the organs of the body. To try to find these empirically—wissen Sie, verstehen Sie—would be useless. We must have recourse to planned chemical synthesis: proceed from a chemical substance with a recognisable activity, make homologues and derivatives of different kinds from it, and try each one of these to discover the degree of its activity and effectiveness.'

His two friends nodded agreement and said:

'There you have found your real life-work: chemistry in medicine!'

Ehrlich was by now excited and quite carried away by his plans.

'Ja, also . . . you see we must take aim—aim by chemical variation! The marvellous effect of an antibody in a serum, as you know, is due to the fact that in no case has it any affinity for the body substances, but it flies straight onward, without deviation, upon the parasites. *The antibodies, therefore, are Magic Bullets, which find their target by themselves.* Hence their astonishingly specific effect, and the advantage of Serum Therapy and of active immunisation over any artificial Chemotherapy. In Chemotherapy we can never count on such complete success and must therefore concentrate all our powers and abilities on making the aim as accurate as we can contrive, so as to strike at the parasites as hard and the body cells as lightly as possible.'

Ehrlich's friends were filled with enthusiasm:

'That is a wonderful idea!'

The next evening, back in Frankfurt, Ehrlich and Professor Bulloch, who was staying another day with him, had dinner together at the Restaurant Buerose on the Bahnhofsplatz opposite the station. Sir Almroth Wright had gone on to London. Ehrlich was at this time 'full of his side-chains', wrote Professor Bulloch in a letter to me, and Ehrlich explained his theories to him during the meal. To make his explanations clearer and more comprehensible to his guest, Ehrlich took a pile of picture post cards which were on the table. He covered these one after another with sketches and diagrams of side-chains, amboceptors, etc. When he had finished with them, he threw the cards on the floor. When the waiter picked them up and counted them to give Ehrlich his bill, he found there were about fifty for which he had to pay. He paid, exclaiming laughingly:

'Oh, really!? . . . Grossartig!' (That's a fine thing!)

In discussions about his theories Ehrlich was generally very lively and animated. Once, when he was explaining his plans and ideas and having an interesting discussion with friends in England in their laboratory, an assistant engaged there, who was used to a quieter approach to scientific questions, regarded Ehrlich's excited manner with some anxiety. Thinking that a really serious quarrel was going on, he asked his chief in a whisper:

'Shall I separate them?'

CHAPTER X

STIMULANTS AND DIVERSIONS

EHRLICH had set himself the task of penetrating the obscure depths of Nature—investigating and discovering new things. He was driven on by an inward urge, not from egoistic motives but from a burning desire to help humanity. His life and work were like a candle burning at both ends. To stand the enormous strain on his physical and intellectual strength he needed 'strong stimulants'—as he himself said, 'starken Tobak' (strong tobaccò)—to prevent him getting tired out. And he needed harmless little diversions, often of a childlike simplicity, to distract his mind from the problems of his work. His 'strong stimulants' were his cigars, which played such an important part in his simple way of life. All day long, and sometimes even during the night, he had to have them.

He preferred those flowers which have a strong scent, such as jasmine, acacia, tuberose and elder. He loved bright colours. A glowing red or yellow gave him intense pleasure, and the sight of a bunch of gay colours would make him quite ecstatic. He was delighted to see broom in the country all covered with golden yellow blossoms, and once when visiting friends in England he admired very much the fine broom which he saw there.

Detective novels were one of his diversions. He liked to read such stories because they could almost entirely distract his attention from his scientific problems. A signed portrait of Conan Doyle hung on the wall of the study in his house, and he spoke with enthusiasm of the Sherlock Holmes stories, of some of which the author sent him a signed copy 'with compliments to my great colleague'. His use of 'the method of Sherlock Holmes' is illustrated by the following story which Sir Henry Dale remembered and kindly told me:

'Robert Koch had never been able to find tubercle bacilli with the microscope in a film of blood, even if this had been taken from a patient in whom a severe tuberculous infection

H 93

was evidently being spread through the circulation. Somebody had sent him, however, a blood film made on a square cover-glass, appropriately stained and mounted on a microscopic slide, in which Koch himself readily confirmed with the micro-scope the presence of bacilli which looked exactly like those of tubercle. This was so contradictory to his own experience that he suspected some technical error, but was quite unable to think of any way in which this might have occurred.

'He asked Ehrlich, then an assistant in his department, to make any examination of the preparation which might throw light on the anomaly. Ehrlich undertook to examine it, if he could be provided with the latest form of *camera lucida* from Zeiss, a mechanical stage for the microscope and the largest obtainable sheets of squared paper. Making a complete map at a high magnification of the whole film on its square cover-slip, and charting separately the position of each one of the tubercle bacilli to be found, he was able to show that they were all in the corners, and that the blood film covering the centre of the slip was entirely free from them. The man who had prepared and submitted the blood film had evidently made it on an old cover-slip, previously used for a film of some material, such as a phthisical sputum, containing many tubercle bacilli; and the slip had been "cleaned" by rubbing it with a cloth, in such a way that the old film was not properly removed at the corners. There the blood film was superposed upon it, so that the tubercle bacilli, left from the previous usage, appeared to be in the blood. Enquiry then enabled the sender of the film to discover that it was, indeed, the practice of his laboratory man to supply him with cover-glasses which had thus been used before, after "cleaning" them in that casual manner. And there, as Ehrlich used to say, you have the method of Sherlock Holmes.'

We said above, that he liked to read such detective stories because they could 'almost entirely' distract his attention from his scientific problems. 'Almost', because even these, like every other book or periodical he read, bore on the inside pages as well as on the cover his notes in coloured pencil, his catchwords and chemical formulae.

Often when reading a scientific article, sent to him by its author, he would write in the margin or on the cover. These articles were frequently heavily underlined and followed by exclamation marks. There were comments such as 'good', 'very good', 'important', 'must be re-read carefully', and sometimes, as his judgment was always given quite frankly: 'miserable'.

When, later on (about 1904) it was decided that the Georg Speyer-Haus should be built, and preparations were made for this, a would-be investigator applied for a position in the new Institute for Experimental Chemotherapy as soon as the work would begin. As a proof of his past work he sent a copy of one of his publications to Ehrlich, and some time later, having had no answer, he asked a friend of his, who at that time was working with Ehrlich, to say a word of recommendation about him. When the friend mentioned the applicant and his paper to Ehrlich, the latter merely pulled a small reprint out of a pile of books on the sofa. He handed it to the friend, who saw the title, with the author's name, and the remark which Ehrlich had made in very large writing on the cover: 'Quatsch!' (Bosh!). This blunt valuation of the work made them both laugh heartily, and the 'case' was dismissed.

Ehrlich often made so many notes and even sketches or drawings of 'side-chains', etc., on books which had been lent to him by friends that he could not send them back to the owners but had to order new copies from the bookshop. But he did not do this until the owner asked for the book. For among his friends it was a proverbial saying that Ehrlich never returned a borrowed book. Of course, this is a fault shared by a great many people, and Ehrlich, knowing of his weakness in this respect, once wrote a short note to Dr. Max Neisser, who, after working with him in his Institute, had become Director of the Hygienic Institute of the University of Frankfurt. The note said:

'Could you let me have a catalogue of the Dresden Hygiene Exhibition? Strangely enough I cannot find my own copy.' He added to this, in his own handwriting: 'Only for *one hour*, so there will be no possibility of loss!!'

With a humorous reference to Ehrlich's negligence with regard to borrowed books, his friend Professor Edinger of Frankfurt University once wrote to him, calling his attention to a new and interesting publication, as follows:

'In case the author has not yet sent you a copy, I think I could possibly make up my mind to lend mine *even to you.*'

And on another occasion Dr. Edinger reminded him: 'We must not lose faith in mankind. There really are people who return borrowed books! Of course, they are rarely to be found, but they do good deeds by their noble manners! Or don't you think so? . . . Kindest regards.'

It must be said that Ehrlich himself bought lots of books, and the expense of these was so great that it required the larger part of the salary which he got from the Prussian Ministry. Ehrlich called himself a 'spendthrift' and said with regard to this in autobiographical notes which he sent to one of his friends in New York:

'I am by Nature anointed with a drop—and a very big drop —of prodigal oil!'

He could not bear to restrict his work for want of materials or animals for experiments. He therefore paid out of his own pocket if there was not enough money for the necessary supplies. For him money meant the saving of time and the possibility of undertaking daring excursions into the intellectual regions where his bold ideas led him. He once compared the flight of his thoughts with rising in the air in a balloon:

'If I then land at an unknown place I know at once what I am going to find there for my work. Nothing else interests me.'

He was kept informed about all new scientific publications by several booksellers; and his orders, sent off at least once a week, always contained ten to twenty items or more. He read everything of importance for his purpose, and knew everything that was going on, although, as he could get a grasp of a subject in a very short time, he might have given to some the impression of reading but little.

Ehrlich invented many words and phrases which have since been permanently adopted in medical terminology. With regard to reading he used to speak of 'diagonal reading.' After Ehrlich's death an English doctor published a fine article about him, but said that he could not quite picture what Ehrlich meant by 'diagonal reading'. It may, I think, be thought of as similar to what an intelligent reader does if he wants to inform himself from the daily newspapers of what is going on: he is acquainted, in general, with the events of the time, and the headlines give an idea of the contents of the different articles. If he is short of time or disinclined to study the entire article he can gather sufficient information by glancing over it diagonally, starting at the top left-hand corner and ending at the bottom on the right. Ehrlich was aware of what was going on in all scientific fields, so that it may have been sufficient for his information just to glance diagonally over the new publications and then, perhaps, with a coloured pencil to make a note here and there in the margin, such as 'must be read minutely' or perhaps . . . 'miserable'.

Ehrlich speaks, also with regard to reading, of an 'affinity' which made him notice everything that had any relation to his scientific problems or to every-day questions which interested him, while at other things he merely glanced. About the most profitable use of literature he said: 'One must follow up certain lines of thought when studying the literature: in that way the literature is fertilising, otherwise only confusing.' But of course only an intuitive genius can make a successful selection. Ehrlich had what he called 'red strands'—leading ideas —which had existed in his mind even in his youth and remained as clues throughout his whole life.

Ehrlich's Absent-mindedness

Ehrlich always worked with the utmost concentration, without heeding what was going on around him. The following amusing little anecdote, which among others about Ehrlich has been much laughed at, may give an idea of his concentration.

The late Professor Reid Hunt of Harvard Medical School, formerly Ehrlich's pupil and then assistant, who worked with him from 1902 to 1904 at the Institute for Experimental Therapy at Frankfurt, wrote to me some time ago about it. In the autumn of 1902 the great French investigator Professor Nocard of the Pasteur Institute had been to visit Ehrlich. They were, as I know myself, very much attached to one another, so much so that when Dr. Nocard suddenly died as the result of a laboratory infection, Ehrlich shed tears of dismay and grief on receiving the news of his death.

Professor Nocard had promised and subsequently sent two of his laboratory rats, which were infected with a certain

experimental strain of Trypanosomiasis. Immediately they
arrived Ehrlich asked Dr. Hunt to make curative experiments
with these rats, giving him on a written 'block' dated
December 1902 the following directions: 'quinine derivatives,
including methylhydrocuprein, some dyestuff preparations and

Dr. Reid Hunt, Ehrlich's Assistant, 1904

Atoxyl.' Dr. Hunt started the experiments, using a great many
rats.

One morning Dr. Hunt came into Ehrlich's laboratory with
his record books and found him very busy with test tube
experiments over the Bunsen burner. Dr. Hunt said cheerfully:

'Good morning, Herr Geheimrat . . .' but stopped suddenly because Ehrlich only looked up at him for a second, nodding kindly, and said, without interrupting his experiment and with his thoughts obviously far away:

'Tag ook, my dear Hunt—was gibts Neues?' (what news have you?).

Dr. Hunt ventured to continue:

'We have no more rats, Herr Geheimrat, to continue the experiments with the trypanosomes. The animal breeder says he cannot supply us with any rats at present.'

Ehrlich, without looking up from his work, said absent-mindedly:

'Hm . . . ja . . . al-so . . . sorry . . . what shall we do, my dear Hunt?'

Dr. Hunt timidly suggested:

'Couldn't we go on with *mice*?'

Ehrlich held the test tube up to the light, examining the contents, continued to boil, always keeping his eye on the dye solution in the tube, and said, without looking at Dr. Hunt:

'Oh no, no, Dr. Hunt . . . that would not do . . . you *must* have rats'—and he nodded decidedly—'*they have tails*!' (N.B. Injections are made into the tail-vein.)

'But mice also have tails, Herr Geheimrat,' Dr. Hunt ventured to say, without moving a muscle of his face.

Earnestly Ehrlich replied:

'Right . . . right my dear Hunt, mice *have* tails—a very good observation!' and he looked at Dr. Hunt with a quick consenting nod. His assistant had to take great pains to keep a solemn face, and hurriedly retired.

Sir Henry Dale of London, who also worked with Ehrlich about 1903–4, recently told me the following story which again illustrates Ehrlich's absent-mindedness when absorbed in his work and thoughts.

The first day after his arrival at Frankfurt, Dale was received and given a hearty welcome by Ehrlich when he visited him at the Serum Institute, and at once found himself listening to a flood of persuasive talk about the experiments which he was to undertake. Not being very familiar yet with the German language, however, young Dale could only with difficulty

follow and grasp the meaning. Ehrlich said he was very sorry
not to be able to invite him to his house for dinner as Frau
Ehrlich was away; but he himself was invited to dine with
friends that evening, and Dale must accompany him as his
friends would be very pleased to meet him. He persuaded his
young visitor to accept this invitation, telling him he would
enjoy a talk with the lady of the house, who spoke English
very well.

That evening, before they left Ehrlich's house to go to these
friends, Ehrlich talked again for some time about all the scien-

Sir Henry Dale about 1908

tific questions that were occupying his mind. Several times the
conversation was interrupted by the housemaid reminding
Ehrlich that it was high time to dress and leave for the party.
Ehrlich never stopped talking the whole time, however, even
when they were going downstairs into the hall and leaving
the house. As they were about to enter the cab that waited
outside, the housemaid called from the door:

'Herr Professor, did you take the money to pay the driver
that I put on the mantelpiece?'

Upon this Ehrlich began to search in all his pockets; but
the maid had already run back into the house and came out
again with the money, handing it, not to Ehrlich, but to the
driver, so that it would not get lost. They started off.

'Yes, but where are we going?' exclaimed Ehrlich excitedly, having already seated himself, and he knocked at the window, calling out:

'Driver, where are we going to?' in answer to which the driver only waved his hand. Breathing a sigh of relief, Ehrlich leaned back again on the seat and said, quite contentedly:

'He knows—Dora told him.'

Then he continued the interrupted scientific conversation without a moment's pause, so that Dale was unable to ask the name of Ehrlich's friends to whom they were going.

The carriage stopped at their house, and as Ehrlich, still talking, was walking up the front steps, a scientific colleague, Dr. Freund, arrived from the other direction. He had also been invited to the house of these friends, and he and Ehrlich greeted each other warmly. They began at once to discuss scientific questions which were of the highest interest to both of them, and hurrying up the steps they went into the house. Having taken off their overcoats they proceeded to the drawing-room upstairs, Ehrlich having completely forgotten Dale, who had followed as closely as he could.

So there he was, standing deserted and alone, a stranger to the town, a stranger to the house, with little knowledge of German, and only admitted by the servants as being obviously with the other two, who were familiar to them. There was nothing to do but try to make himself understood and inquire the name of the family in whose house he was a guest. Finally he was taken upstairs and entered the drawing-room where the hostess, Frau Oppenheim, came forward with a greeting of charming friendliness for 'Ehrlich's young Englishman'. Presently Ehrlich, by that time deep in discussion with his famous cousin Carl Weigert, looked up and saw Dale talking to Frau Oppenheim. Extending both his arms in his excitement, and exclaiming:

'Oh, my goodness! My dear Dr. Dale, I had completely forgotten you!' he came forward to make the belated introduction.

Sir Henry Dale also told me recently of the following amusing incident, which occurred during his stay in Frankfurt. Ehrlich had offered, as was always his first impulse, his precious imported cigars to a visitor, who declined, however, saying that he did not smoke. Ehrlich went on talking animatedly, and presently renewed the offer:

'A cigar, Herr Kollege?'

'No thank you, I do not smoke,' repeated the visitor.

'Oh, you do not smoke!' said Ehrlich, quite astonished. 'Then may I offer you a glass of wine?' (This in spite of the fact that he never kept wine at the Institute.)

'No, thank you very much,' said the visitor. 'I happen to be a teetotaller.'

'Perhaps a glass of water then?'

'Yes, please, a glass of water,' said the visitor, anxious to please Ehrlich and not refuse again.

'Kadereit!' Ehrlich at once called out, having opened the door a crack, and then went on talking to the visitor.

When Kadereit came running, Ehrlich muttered, half to himself:

'Now what was it I wanted to ask Kadereit?'

The visitor, reminding him, said:

'A glass of water for me, Herr Geheimrat.'

'Oh yes, a glass of water for you,' said Ehrlich. But when Kadereit brought the glass of mineral water on a little tray, Ehrlich absent-mindedly took it, put it on the floor beside him, and began to drink from it now and then as he continued his voluble exposition to the visitor. This went on until, with the glass of water finished, he noticed that the visitor was not smoking, and again reached for and offered the box of cigars!

Sir Henry Dale, when I recently had the pleasure of seeing him, gave me one of Ehrlich's famous 'blocks' with instructions and suggestions for the day's work. Like most of Ehrlich's handwritten notes, it is almost illegible. When we tried together, and finally succeeded in deciphering it, Sir Henry recalled how, when he was in Frankfurt, all Ehrlich's collaborators and assistants at the Serum Institute were accustomed to meet every morning in the laboratory of Professor Apolant, of the Cancer Research Department, bringing with them their sandwiches for their 'zweites Frühstück' (English 'elevenses') and the 'blocks' they had received that morning from Ehrlich but had been unable to decipher. Professor Apolant was known to have a special gift for reading Ehrlich's handwriting; he was the Institute's recognised expert in this matter. But even he sometimes found it difficult, and then he would hold the 'block' aloft in his upraised right hand because

One of Ehrlich's 'blocks'

Es wäre wohl zweckmässig, wenn Sie auch die vitale *Methylenblau—* (Färbung) der affizierten Nervenstämme mit in den Bereich der Untersuchungen ziehen wollten. E. (The word 'Färbung' is omitted)

It would perhaps be profitable if you would also take the vital dyeing with methylene blue into the field of your investigations. E.

held at some distance from the eye, a script thus forms a picture and is often more legible than at closer range. When on such occasions Professor Apolant succeeded in discovering the meaning of a message he would call out triumphantly:

'Now I have got it! . . . that must mean . . .' Then the tense features of the men around him would relax and look contented

Professor Herter

and happy, for now everyone knew what Ehrlich wanted him to do.

On two other blocks which Sir Henry showed me, written at intervals of a few months, the note merely said:

'How are your experiments going on?'

Ehrlich never forgot what experiments he had suggested, and inquired of his fellow-workers concerning their progress from time to time.

Ehrlich never pronounced Sir Henry Dale's name correctly, but always in the German way, and said: 'Dear Dr. Dahlee'. This amused Professor Herter of New York, who was at the same time working with Ehrlich in his Institute. He had his family also with him in Frankfurt, and the Herters (the professor, his wife and his three daughters) used to address Dr. Dale even in later years for fun as 'Dear Dr. Dahlee'.

CHAPTER XI

LECTURES AND PUBLICATIONS

DAYS and dates meant little to Ehrlich. He never paid much attention to them and very unwillingly interrupted his work for a little recreation. Sundays and holidays he liked best, for

Plaque dedicated to Ehrlich by his assistants and collaborators on his fiftieth birthday, 14 March, 1904

then he could work more undisturbed than during the week. When he finally consented, after being implored by his wife and friends to take a little rest, he would ask, before the train which was to take him to his holiday had even started: 'What date is it to-day?' and then begin to count the days until his return. He was always very glad to get back again to his laboratory.

Only a few journeys to give lectures and occasionally to attend an international congress in a foreign country could keep Ehrlich a little longer away from his work, and then only at rare intervals. In 1900 he gave in England the 'Croonian Lecture,' to the Royal Society, 'On Immunity with Special Reference to Cell Life'. According to Professor William Bulloch, he took his English colleagues by storm, when, on the occasion of this visit, he delivered enthusiastic speeches on 'Old Lister'.

In 1904 Ehrlich received an invitation to go to New York and Baltimore to give the 'Herter Lectures', and following these he also delivered lectures in Washington and Chicago.

All his lectures were given in German. He spoke German with foreign colleagues visiting him in Frankfurt and also answered in German letters written to him in other languages. His foreign friends wrote to him in English or French; French he read easily and even spoke it nicely, but English he spoke not at all, and even read but little. When an English paper interested him, he often sought the service of a colleague who knew the language better, to get it translated. When a visitor did not know any German, Ehrlich spoke French, or asked one of his collaborators to act as interpreter. For English I was called upon to help, and on such occasions he introduced me good-naturedly as his 'right and left hand'. Once he was showing the machine for producing artificial ice to an American scientist who was interested to see everything at the Institute. As Ehrlich pronounced the word 'ice' as 'izze' the visitor did not, of course, understand what he meant. Then Ehrlich laughed at himself and declared that he had 'no head for foreign languages'.

Whenever Ehrlich had to undertake writings of any length, for lectures or publications, he needed a lot of prompting to make him get on with them and would not start the work until the very last moment. Publishers would write and telegraph imploringly reminding him that the promised manuscript was overdue. Quite unperturbed, he would postpone delivery until a later date, promising to send it in by then

without fail. Often, as that date approached, he would again
send telegrams excusing further delay. But it gave him a great
deal of simple pleasure when he was able to send in a manu-

Ehrlich aged fifty

script almost by the promised date. This was so rare an occurrence that on one such occasion he could not deny himself the
delight of writing to the editor of the *Deutsche Medizinische
Wochenschrift*, Dr. Schwalbe of Berlin: 'How do I stand now?
A man of my word!'

However, when a manuscript *had* to be finished, at the eleventh hour so to speak, Ehrlich would dictate it in one mighty effort without a break, and without making a rough draft first. He would only have a few key-words noted on a 'block', underlined in coloured pencil and marked with exclamation or question marks. The manuscripts of his lectures and scientific publications are extraordinary, only now and then a marginal note in coloured pencil or the underlining of a particularly important word or phrase. It was never necessary for a report, lecture, professional opinion or article for a scientific journal to be re-written, and in those fields of investigation which, like Chemotherapy, were nearest to his heart, he made especially few alterations. His ability as a writer is in strange contrast with his manner when lecturing, for on the platform he was not a brilliant speaker.

Professor Reid Hunt has reminded me that some months before his trip to America in 1904, Ehrlich used this coming event as a pretext, telling visitors that he was in a great hurry as he had to write his lectures for America. Not one word of these lectures was written, however, and Dr. Hunt predicted that Ehrlich would not begin to write them until the ship on which he was travelling had left the shores of Europe. After he had arrived at Baltimore, Dr. Hunt, who had returned to his American home, came to see Ehrlich at his hotel about an hour before the first lecture was to be given.

'You wronged me, my dear Hunt, by saying that I should write my lectures on the steamer,' said Ehrlich as soon as he saw him. 'I did nothing of the kind,' he went on. 'I am just writing the first one now.'

Dr. Hunt wrote to me concerning this visit to the United States, saying that Ehrlich was received everywhere with the greatest affection and enthusiasm.

'To everyone with whom he spoke he gave inspiration and encouragement for his work, and his visit was of extraordinary importance to American science.'

In an obituary article published in the *Therapie der Gegenwart*, Berlin, October 1915, which recently came into my hands, Dr. B. Laquer of Wiesbaden said about this visit of Ehrlich's to the United States:

'Professor William H. Welch, of the Johns Hopkins Medical

School, Baltimore, the reformer of medical education in the U.S.A. and an old friend and admirer of Ehrlich from their time together in Breslau, said that some kind of 'irradiation' inspiring enthusiasm in his audiences, emanated from Ehrlich when he appeared and lectured in New York, Baltimore and Chicago in 1904.'

Ehrlich came back from this trip filled with an equal enthusiasm. He was charmed by the simple kindness and practical good sense of the American people. It is reported that he showed so much interest in everything and asked so many questions that his wife was a little embarrassed about it and tried to stop him. On the occasion of a dinner in his honour, when his questions seemed to be unending, she whispered to him:

'But Paul, the Americans must think that we are very inquisitive!'

At this Ehrlich turned to his friend, Professor William H. Welch, and asked him, smiling:

'My dear Welch, am I really *very* inquisitive?'

He was much amused when Dr. Welch answered:

'Well, in scientific questions, a little!'

Ehrlich was very much impressed by the education of American youth, and said:

'America finds youth worthy of esteem and appreciation. With us, in Europe, youth is like a Sibylline book.'

He had definite opinions of his own about the education and bringing up of children. Despite his great love of Latin and the high esteem in which he held humanistic, especially Greek, education, he was not a supporter of the traditional classical schooling. He did not openly oppose it, but he stood aside from all movements propagating this kind of education, as it was understood in Germany at that time, and refused to give his name to printed appeals in favour of classical education. The reforms which he favoured were simplification of writing, simplification of teaching methods and plans, and the adaptation of those methods to develop the natural gifts of the individual child. He believed in giving a child a more practical education in accordance with its talents, rather than driving a 'useless store of knowledge' into the child's little head which it would carry along with it all its life as an unnecessary burden.

Ehrlich anticipated educational reforms long before they were actually brought about. He always called himself a 'monoman'—a man with a single purpose—in spite of his astonishing versatility. He used to declare that a man can only succeed in life when he tries to be as perfect as possible within a certain limited field of work and does not cast his net too wide. Ehrlich cautiously avoided storing up knowledge which he was sure he would never need, and always worked on the following principle: 'Restrict knowledge to what is really necessary; everything beyond this will do harm.' Even in science he believed that individual education was what was needed. 'For investigations in immunity, knowledge of anatomy of the brain is absolutely unnecessary; a boy who wants to study medicine does not need to learn the Greek language; a child with a talent for art and music must not have a dry professional training.'

Ehrlich himself had found school a disagreeable obligation, and although he had received some special prizes he had never had the slightest interest in certain subjects, such as geography. He had always had difficulties at school in finding the correct German expression for his compositions. Examinations he dreaded, and only passed them with such difficulty that speaking of them later he would say, jokingly: 'I only passed examinations by using tricks . . .' What really happened, of course, was that in some respects his knowledge was so brilliant that he had sufficient good marks to balance the negative side of his account.

The simplification of handwriting, which he advocated in the education of children, he had adopted for himself at an early age, as is shown in his first thesis. He always used small Roman letters, only using capitals after a full stop and for proper names. He also used very few punctuation marks. These habits were very unusual in a writer of German. Another peculiarity of his was that he usually put no date on his letters, and never put in the year.

Ehrlich always wrote with a long thick penholder—about 12 inches in length—with a special giant nib about 2 inches long. One of his schoolmates at college in Breslau said that Ehrlich first attracted his attention because he used such a nib almost 5 cm. (2 inches) in length.

Quite often, when he himself wrote orders for books, etc., the bookseller could not read either the title of the book, the rest of the order, or the name and address of the customer. The shop would accordingly cut out the name and address, stick it on a postcard in the hope that the postman could read it, and write on the other side that it was impossible to make out the name and address, that payment must be made in advance and that the sender must write more legibly when sending the money!

All Ehrlich's letters, scientific as well as personal, were friendly and informal in style, showing the greatest amiability and full of appreciation for every kindness shown to him.

Whenever he was answering a letter containing especially pleasing news he would dictate his thanks in reply as if he were face to face with the writer and could convey his pleasure and gratitude to him personally. It was the same when he was speaking on the telephone, for he would gesticulate, bow and smile during the conversation, as animatedly as if the person he was talking to were in the room beside him. This little characteristic recalls what was said about Goethe: that when he was working out a play he would imagine the characters around him in his study, tell them the rôles they had to play, and talk to these imaginary actors as though he were speaking to real people.

Great Kindness and Consideration

At the beginning of my work for Ehrlich a trivial event occurred which upset him very much. It was this: without thinking, I had carelessly written on both sides of a 'block', instead of on only one side. When he saw this, Ehrlich got very excited and cried out reproachfully:

'Look at that! How *could* you do such a thing?'

I took the offending 'block' from him and, as there was nowhere else to put it, placed it on the edge of a chair next to his desk, already piled high with books. I apologised, saying:

'I am sorry, Herr Geheimrat, it was careless of me. It shall not happen again.'

Ehrlich did not reply, but continued to dictate, marching up and down the room as he did so.

'Here also we often find a grouping which brings about the primary binding——' He broke off abruptly, remembering my mistake and said: 'Now, look—look—how *could* you?—Now where were we?'

'Which brings about the primary binding,' I repeated.

'Oh yes. Such a binding or anchoring I call the primary haptophore, the others the secondary haptophores. Here I should like to emphasize especially——' Again he broke off and began muttering angrily: 'Look, look!' and it suddenly dawned on me that every time Ehrlich turned he saw the spoiled 'block' on the chair and was irritated afresh. He had just turned his back again, so I quickly picked up the 'block' and hid it under my note-book. Then he became calm and repeated: '——like to emphasize that we have found only a few chemical compounds which are capable of . . .' Again he stopped; but this time he disappeared into his laboratory adjoining the study, saying as he went:

'*One* moment!'

After a little while, as he did not return, I followed him and stood there with my note-book in my hand ready to continue. But Ehrlich paid no attention to me. He was heating a solution over the Bunsen burner and shaking the test tube from time to time. Without looking up he handed the tube to me, took another one and started a fresh experiment. This test tube he also handed to me, and then a third. I put down my note-book and moved closer to the big laboratory table. Soon I had both hands full of test tubes containing solutions of different colours, so that I could not hold any more. Ehrlich had said nothing about what was to be done with them, so I put them quietly and carefully into the wooden box near the burner where the used tubes were generally placed. Ehrlich continued experimenting, without looking up. Now and then he held the resulting mixture in the tube up to the light, examining it minutely, and saying:

'Schön! Nicht?' (Beautiful, isn't it?)

To this I could only answer: 'Yes'.

'Now, a little more hydrochlor . . .'

I handed him the bottle from the shelf between the two windows. He added some to the mixture and looked at it, holding the test tube up to the light.

'Still a little more. . . . He heated and shook the tube again, and then said enthusiastically

'Beautiful! A marvellous reaction!'

He moved over to the large sheets of white blotting-paper hanging from the shelf on the opposite wall, and poured down upon them, several times, small quantities of the liquid. He looked attentively at the colours which ran out, forming different shades at the edges. Suddenly he said:

'E. Merck, Darmstadt . . .'

I quickly got my note-book and wrote at his dictation:

'Dear Sirs: In reply to your inquiry about the indican reaction, I should like to inform you that the reaction is made in the following way: the reagent consists of equal parts of fuming hydrochloric acid and water, to which $\frac{1}{3}\%$ dimethylamido-benzaldehyde is added. This reagent keeps indefinitely. To prove the presence of indican, about equal parts of urine and reagent are taken (1 to 1·5 c.cs. of urine is sufficient) and then brought to the boil (for the separation of the indican and the colour synthesis). This solution, which generally has a dirty-brown colour, is cooled down: then a minim of strong ammonia and concentrated potassium hydroxide solution is added to it. A beautiful red colouring results, the strength of which gives a measure of the quantity of indican present.

'The essential part of this method is that the dyestuff which results from the union of indoxyl and the aldehyde is soluble with an intensely red colour. The test is very exact and simple, and can be made with a very small quantity of urine.

'I am not yet quite sure what the title of the paper on this subject will be. I should be obliged therefore if you would take that part of my letter which you may need for your reports, saying that it comes to you from private information. With kind regards, Yours very truly,' etc.

Because of his helpful attitude towards them, Ehrlich was able to get from all the big chemical concerns anything he asked for in the way of special chemical preparations and rare substances, even if they had to be specially made for him with great difficulty and at a cost out of all proportion to the small quantity finally produced. This unique collection of chemicals which Ehrlich possessed was his special pride. He regarded 'a big collection of chemical preparations and many experiments' as the first essential to enable the born chemical inventor to do successful work. But besides these requirements there must also be what Ehrlich called the 'Four Big G's': Geduld, Geschick, Geld and Glück. (Patience, Ability, Money and Good Luck.)

Ehrlich spared no effort if he could help a friend or colleague, and he willingly even gave samples of chemical compounds from this precious collection of rare substances. He was equally ready to give animals inoculated with particular strains of tumours or trypanosomes to those who wanted to undertake experiments themselves. Very rarely did he refuse something he was asked for, as rarely, indeed, as he would selfishly hold back his opinion.

This is what Felix Pinkus said:

'He would give plentifully from the free-flowing source of his ideas, and take up readily into the stream of his own thoughts what others had to offer; though in the end he always gave infinitely more to others than he received in return. The abundance of his ideas was much too great for him to care about little formalities. What he left behind him, and what he lavished in the free expression of his thoughts, was enough for many others to live on and enrich themselves by.'

Professor William Bulloch, one of his great friends in London, once wrote to me:

'Never did I ask something of him that he did not with pleasure grant immediately; and a hundred times he bestowed upon me, unasked, the most precious kindness. He was the most extraordinary man I have ever met; with his wonderful inspiration, his enormous power of work, his astonishing know-ledge, he was the greatest man in the medical world of his time, and more of a genius than any other person. Paul Ehrlich was in his innermost soul modest, sincere, noble-minded, and with the greatest kindness and consideration towards everybody. I am convinced that every one of my countrymen who ever came into contact with him has the same feelings towards him as I have.'

Ehrlich's own saying shows his broad-mindedness in scientific questions. It is this:

'One must not stay in a field of work until the crops are

completely brought in, but leave still some part of the harvest for the others.'

His many lovable qualities, his heartiness and the kindliness which he so generously bestowed on even the youngest of his assistants and colleagues, brought him the love and affection of every one. His Institutes at Frankfurt, the setting for his life's work, were not only highly appreciated but renowned in the whole scientific world. Crowds of young investigators came from all parts of the globe. His Institutes were a sort of Mecca which no medical scientist who happened to come to Central Europe would fail to visit.

CHAPTER XII

SERUMTHERAPY AND CHEMOTHERAPY

$$As = As$$

$$NH_2 \quad \overset{}{\underset{OH}{\bigcirc}} \quad \overset{}{\underset{OH}{\bigcirc}} \quad NH_2$$

FROM 1906 onwards Ehrlich's work was mainly dedicated to building up Chemotherapy, the principles and problems of which had been developing in his mind since his days as a young student when the idea had first, as he himself said, 'enchanted' him. His task was the study, production and introduction into medicine, of chemical compounds which would act as specifics for human diseases due to infections: which would really 'cure' these by eliminating the causes and not merely relieve the symptoms of the disease.

In contrast to the use of immune sera in the treatment of *bacterial* infections, where vaccine-therapy was highly efficacious and, in Ehrlich's opinion, the 'ideal treatment', Chemotherapy, as Ehrlich conceived it, had to take account of the action of appropriate artificial chemical compounds upon the *body-cells* as well as upon the disease-producing *parasites*; their 'organo-tropic' as well as their 'parasitotropic' affinities must be studied, with the object of finding and introducing into medicine chemical compounds which are maximally 'parasitotropic' for the particular organisms causing the infection, and minimally 'organotropic' for the tissues of the infected subject.

Starting with his very first work as a student, his dissertation, his studies on 'Vital Staining', on 'The Constitution, Distribution and Action of Chemical bodies', and his 'Side-Chain Theory', there is a line running through these and other publications such as 'The Need of Oxygen by the Organism', 'Anaemia', and his treatises on 'Diagnosis of the Diseases of the Blood', to mention only some of the most important. This line leads straight to Chemotherapy, the vast territory of his last investigations.

Of the development of this subject Ehrlich said:

'I have been led onward upon this path by the "vital dye-stuff injections" in which it is very easy to watch the distribution of the dyes both macroscopically and microscopically, and in which, according to the constitution of the dye applied, very different localisations can be observed. Especially interesting in this connection is methylene blue. This dye has a special relationship to the living nerve fibres, so that on a freshly cut out piece of tissue one can follow up the distribution of the dye into their very finest ramifications. This is even possible with the living animal! The experimenter can stain the parasite which is sucking blood from the urinary bladder of the frog; after injecting the frog he can see a tiny worm, all the muscles and nerves of which are stained blue, creeping about under the microscope. And more than that! In the embryos which fill the body of the frog one can see the outlines of the muscular and nervous system as a very fine blue ring, from which, at regular distances, vertical fibres go out which end upon the surface of the embryo. On the other hand neutral-red is able to stain the so-called granules of the cell in almost all cells of the organism; while another dye, pyrrol blue (which is produced by condensation of tetra-methyl-diamido-benzo-phenol and pyrrol) only stains the granules of one particular kind of cell. Anyone who has seen such pictures with their wonderful display and distinctness will be immediately convinced of the necessity of regarding the distribution of such substances, within the finest elements, as the basis of pharmacological investigation.

'In this way I have distinguished neurotropic, lipotropic and polytropic dyes, according to whether they are stored in or bound to the nervous system, the adipose tissue, etc., of the living organism. A substance can act upon the brain only when it is neurotropic, upon a parasite only when it is parasito-tropic. Starting from these conceptions, I have tried to penetrate into the darkness of the investigation of immunity; and my conceptions of the primary anchoring of toxin brought me to the principle of *specific binding* and, leading on from this, to the so-called "*Side-Chain Theory*." '

About chemotherapeutic work in general Ehrlich said:

'The whole field of research is governed by a quite simple,

I should like to say self-evident, natural principle. If in Chemistry the fundamental law is "corpora non agunt nisi liquida", in Chemotherapy it must be: "corpora non agunt nisi fixata". This would mean that parasites can only be killed by those substances to which they have a certain relationship, which binds or anchors the substance to the parasite. Such substances I call "parasitotropic". But all substances which destroy parasites are also, as already mentioned, poisons: that is, they have relationship to organs of vital importance. Thus they are, at the same time, also "organotropic". It is quite evident that only those substances in which the "organotropism" and "parasitotropism" stand in a well-balanced relation to each other can be used in practical medicine as "curative substances". To go forward it was necessary not to be content with such first ideas, but to penetrate deeper into the mechanism and find out in what way the drugs are fixed to the cell-organs. It was the work on trypanosomes and especially the minute examination of the drug-resistant stains which led to definite conceptions about the process of "fixation".'

Ehrlich gave this definition of the difference between Serumtherapy and Chemotherapy:

'We have, in active and passive immunisation, a powerful weapon which has already shown its effectiveness in many infectious diseases and always will do so. What makes Serumtherapy so extraordinarily active is the fact that the protecting substances of the body are products of the organism itself, and that they act purely parasitotropically and not organotropically. Here we may speak of *"magic bullets"* which aim exclusively at the dangerous intruding parasites strangers to the organism, but do not touch the organism itself and its cells. Serumtherapy is therefore obviously, wherever it can be carried out, superior to any other mode of action!

'But we know of a number of infectious diseases, especially those which are caused by protozoa, where Serumtherapy either does not work at all or only with much loss of time. I call attention especially to malaria, to the diseases caused by trypanosomes, and perhaps a number of infections caused by spirilla must be counted here too. In these cases chemical substances must come to aid the treatment! Instead of Serumtherapy, Chemotherapy must be used.

'In order to use Chemotherapy successfully we must search for substances which have an affinity to the cells of the parasites and a power of killing them greater than the damage such substances cause to the organism itself, so that the destruction of the parasites will be possible without seriously hurting the organism. This means that we must strike the parasites and the parasites only, if possible, and to do this, we must learn to aim, learn to aim with chemical substances! The methods which have been worked out offer the possibility of obtaining, by chemical synthesis, a rich variety of those chemical substances.'

In the light of Ehrlich's conception of these questions, the curative action seems to be only an expression of a special form of distribution which is most favourable in those instances where the chemical substance has the maximum affinity to the parasites causing the infection but causes the minimum of harm to the sick organism. For all the chemical substances which he tried out, Ehrlich set up a standard with regard to the proper relation between the healing dose—'*dosis curative*' and the maximal tolerated dose—'*dosis tolerata*'. This relation he called 'therapeutic coefficient', or 'therapeutic index'.

About his own particular way of working we can do best by referring again to his autobiographical notes already mentioned. Ehrlich says there:

'During my work as a student I repeatedly tried to follow up certain lines of thought by experiment. But I did not succeed in carrying out a single one of my ideas in this way. Soon, however, I came to try the other way round, that is to say, not to give directions to Nature but simply try to analyse striking experimental facts which were difficult to understand and by so analysing to find the laws which governed the action.

'I have always found it important to get thoroughly acquainted with the physiological, chemical and biological character of many substances. For only by intensive work carried on during years is it possible to gather that knowledge which is necessary to work successfully in a certain field of research later on and, as I call it, to foretell.

'I believe that for every one who wants to work chemotherapeutically this is indispensable, for in this manner a

multitude of details will be gathered and stored in the sub-
conscious; and this will automatically, at the right time,
set him on the right track. So it was, for instance, with the
invention of trypan-red which belongs to the benzopurpurine
series: I had often noticed that benzopurpurines remain such
a long time in the organism and I hoped that this series would
be able to do something particular. Then, when I came to
study Trypanosomiasis, benzopurpurine was among the first
substances to be tried out. It showed in the experiment little,
though definite, influence and I had the idea that this weak
effect must be caused by its somewhat difficult solubility.
Therefore I asked Dr. Arthur von Weinberg to have it made
more easily soluble by introducing the solubilising action of
the sulphonic acid group. This done . . . and the trypan-red
was found!

'Also, with regard to Arsenophenylglycin (418) I had con-
sciously made a note in my "blocks", foretelling its chemical
construction. I put up the programme: to make the molecule
at its upper side, i.e. the arsenical radicle, more poisonous by
reduction; and *at the lower side*, at the amino-group; *less*
poisonous by the introduction of acid-radicles.'

.   .   .   .

At the beginning of the century the first preparations to be
tried out were those which Dr. Ludwig Benda had made according to Ehrlich's directions in the Cassella Chemical Works
at Frankfurt-Mainkur. (These works later on became part of
the I.G. Farben Company.) Dr. Arthur von Weinberg, Director of the Cassella Works, had for a long time been a personal
friend and a sponsor of Ehrlich. He had ordered Dr. Benda to
put himself entirely at Ehrlich's disposal, as it was not possible
to do chemical work in the Serum Institute. Among these substances which Dr. Benda prepared there was a red benzidine
dye, trypan-red, and a yellow acridine dye, trypaflavine,
which both showed good results in animal experiments on
trypanosome infections. The trypan-red being the stronger and
more effective, it was also tried in the tropics and had some
success in curing the natives suffering from the African Sleeping-Sickness, due to a trypanosome infection. The animal
experiments were made in the Serum Institute, under Ehr-

Ehrlich's friend Dr. Arthur von Weinberg

Dr. Ludwig Benda

lich's supervision, by Dr. Shiga, a pupil of Professor Kitasato of Tokio.

Professor Kitasato had studied and done scientific work in Europe for a long time both at the Pasteur Institute in Paris, with Ehrlich in the Robert Koch Institute, and with von Behring in Berlin. He shared with von Behring the research work on Diphtheria and Tetanus antitoxin, and they published together their first findings in 1890.[1] After that he returned to

At work in the laboratory with Dr. Shiga (third from the left)

his home in Tokio and soon founded there an Institute like the Pasteur Institute which he called the 'Tokio Institute for Infectious Diseases'. The Pasteur Institute had also been taken as a model for the 'Robert Koch Institute for Infectious Diseases' in Berlin. Soon after his return home Kitasato began to send his best and ablest Japanese pupils to the most important institutes for scientific research at that time: the Pasteur Institute in Paris, the Robert Koch Institute in Berlin and to

[1] 'Behring und Kitasato. Ueber das Zustandekommen der Diphtherie-Immunität und der Tetanus-Immunität bei Tieren. (Aus dem Hygienischen Institut des Herrn Geh. Rat Koch in Berlin).' *Deutsche Medizinische Wochenschrift*, 1890, No. 49, 4 Dezember.

Ehrlich in Frankfurt, in order to increase their knowledge of medical science.

The first of these pupils to come to Ehrlich was Dr. Shiga. He worked under the direction of Ehrlich from 1902 to 1905,

Ehrlich in 1905

and then the time came for his return to Tokio. Ehrlich, as always, was absorbed in his test tube experiments. His cigar had gone out, many solutions had been heated and shaken, and he had searched for and found some special substances in his precious chemical collection, when Dr. Shiga came into the laboratory to say good-bye. Ehrlich nodded affably to him and said:

'Tag ook, my dear Shiga. Anything new?'

Dr. Shiga handed over to him, with the customary deep bow of the Japanese, his books with the records of his animal experiments. Ehrlich looked at them, turning the pages and regarding the notes carefully. Then he said, with a kindly smile:

'Finished! Fine experiments, my dear Shiga.'

Dr. Shiga, very pleased, bowed repeatedly and said:

'Trypan-red very effective; . . . cures infection with trypano-somes.'

'Yes,' replied Ehrlich, speaking slower and more clearly as he usually did so that Dr. Shiga would understand more easily. 'Yes, I have also received reports from East Africa from Professor Kleine and Dr. von Raven of *very good* results with trypan-red —and from Professor Iversen of Petersburg as well, who has found very good healing results in cases of relapsing fever and Spirillosis of chickens—and even in *human* cases of the diseases.'

Dr. Shiga looked very glad, bowed and remarked again:

'Very good . . . very effective . . . trypan-red!'

Then Kadereit came in and announced that Dr. Franke had arrived.

'Please show him in,' said Ehrlich. Dr. Shiga wanted to retire, but Ehrlich said with a kindly gesture:

'Please, my dear Shiga,—einen Augenblick!' (just a moment).

Dr. Franke, a young man of medium height with bright features and sparkling eyes, came into the room.

'Tag ook, dear Dr. Franke. A-l-s-o, you wish to work with us here. . . . I am told you are a Silesian. . . . *Do people really come from Silesia?*'

Dr. Franke looked stupefied at this, until Ehrlich went on with an amused little laugh:

'Wissen Sie, I, too, come from Silesia!'

Then Dr. Franke also smiled and answered promptly: 'All the best people come from Silesia!'

Ehrlich burst out laughing and then said:

'This is Dr. Shiga, who is going to leave us now. He goes back to Tokio to the Institute for Infectious Diseases . . . and I should like *you* now to continue the experiments with our

K

preparations . . . wissen Sie . . .; verstehen Sie (you know, you understand) . . . trypan-red . . . that has really given very good results in the treatment of animals and also human patients with trypanosome infections and relapsing fever . . . you must work with mice . . . but also go on with the treatment of monkeys. . . .'

Dr. Franke nodded affirmatively during this address, Dr. Shiga kept on bowing and Ehrlich, the record book in one hand and a coloured pencil in the other, kept tapping first one and then the other on the arms and shoulders.

Eventually both Dr. Shiga and Dr. Franke retired, Dr. Shiga with a final deep bow. As he left, Ehrlich repeated to Dr. Franke, tapping him on the sleeve of his coat with his spectacles:

'Dear Dr. Franke, remember—much experimenting—the utmost exactitude in experiments—the absolute minimum of hypothesis—much work—no guesswork—few publications—and no "advance information"—wissen Sie—verstehen Sie. . . .' (you know, you understand).

Dr. Franke nodded.

CHAPTER XIII

THE GEORG SPEYER-HAUS

EHRLICH was able to interest the wealthy Frau Franziska
Speyer, of the well-known Frankfurt family Speyer-Ellissen, in

*Frau Franziska Speyer who built and endowed
the Georg Speyer-Haus for Ehrlich's work in
Chemotherapy*

the work which held such promise of success. Frau Speyer
decided to help him, and a new institute was built for the
exclusive purpose of furthering Ehrlich's chemotherapeutical
researches. In addition to financing the building of the new

institute, Frau Speyer also made a generous grant to cover the current expenses of the work. The Georg Speyer-Haus for Chemotherapy, so called in memory of her late husband, was built on ground belonging to the City of Frankfurt, adjoining the 'Serum Institute', with the big buildings and the gardens of the Frankfurt Hospital behind it. The new building was

The Institute for Experimental Therapy ('Serum Institute') and the George Speyer-Haus, Paul Ehrlichstrasse 42–44, Frankfurt a.M.

opened and dedicated to its purpose in the early summer of 1906.

Ehrlich now had two large institutes for scientific research to superintend, and to inspire with his genius and his enthusiasm. Life could not remain as calm as it had been when he first came to Frankfurt, when all these new tasks had still been merely ardent wishes cherished in his mind, with no means as yet to work them out at the pace which was characteristic of him and which he liked. Now he had to look after everything that went on in *both* institutes, and that meant twice as much work and responsibility as before.

He now began systematically to examine a great number of

Part of a sixteen-page letter about the building of the new institute from Ehrlich to Frau Speyer's brother-in-law chemical substances according to the aforesaid principles: dye-stuffs of the benzidine, triphenylmethane and acridine series, and then arsenical compounds. Ehrlich had begun his work in this important field at his Institute for Experimental Therapy, or 'Serum-Institute', as a natural consequence and continuation of his work on his 'Side-Chain Theory'.

After working at home in the early morning, Ehrlich used to arrive at his laboratory shortly after 10 a.m. He would then immediately visit all the different sections of both his Institutes, with the exception of those which could work independently, such as the 'Section for Control of the Serum Preparations for Human and Animal Treatment', which was run according to State regulations. The head of the section was always a military medical officer delegated by the Government. Then there was the Serological Section, which had to attend to all the Wassermann-reaction tests for the hospitals and doctors of Frankfurt; and here the scientific work on problems of serology and immunity was carried on.

Ehrlich controlled all current experiments of the Chemical and Biological Sections of the George Speyer-Haus, and the Cancer Section of the Serum Institute, and gave instructions for new experiments and methods.

His rounds ended about one o'clock, and I shall always remember how he looked as he returned from the Speyer-Haus, which was separated from the Serum Institute only by a small fenced garden. He would have the little box containing twenty-five cigars pressed tightly under his left arm, and in his right hand his thick-rimmed spectacles which he balanced or swung about, holding them by one of the strong side-pieces, and gazing straight ahead of him, yet with an inward look, entirely wrapt up in his thoughts. Without an overcoat even in winter, often without even a hat, he heeded neither rain nor snow nor stormy weather. He made a deeply impressive picture of a scientific investigator who had dedicated himself completely to the task of searching—and finding.

At the entrance of the Serum Institute he would call out, so that it resounded down the long corridor, for Kadereit to bring him mineral water or cigars. Kadereit always responded promptly.

Then came all the clerical work which had to be attended

to: the enormously extensive correspondence, and all the other writing which was an important part of the day's work and to which much time and great care was dedicated. But, however busy he was with this, and with the chemical experiments at which he very often continued to work while he was dictating, he always found time for visitors and had long conversations with them.

If a colleague, perhaps a scientist from abroad, came to see him and ask his advice about his own experiments, Ehrlich listened most attentively. With a few questions and answers he would, however, very quickly grasp the problem; and if the visitor then continued with lengthy and unnecessary explanations, Ehrlich would soon grow silent and only appear to pay attention by making an occasional remark such as: 'Oh yes,' or 'Wirklich?' (Really?). Felix Pinkus gives a very good description of this:

'To those who knew him, it was most instructive to observe how Ehrlich, while apparently listening intently to the visitor who brought him a detailed description of his problems, had already grasped the matter after a few remarks and, long before the visitor had finished, Ehrlich's mind had gone on to other things. It always seemed to me one of the most amazing things about his brain, how he could—while surely thinking meanwhile of something quite different—nevertheless remember afterwards every word of what the visitor said.

'In conversation his thoughts always galloped one after the other in rapid succession, so much so that only those who were accustomed to his way of speaking were able to follow the way his mind switched from one idea to another. To those who did not know him he gave the impression of being an "absent-minded professor" who would forget everything and go through life ignorant of practical things; yet he was, in his world-famous scientific institutes, one of the most ingenious practitioners who ever lived.'

When talking with his colleagues and assistants who understood him, Ehrlich spoke very quickly and animatedly, and never pompously, and when his mind was entirely filled with a certain idea he would even address visitors with less scientific knowledge in the same lively, energetic way. He perceived the idea as if it had a physical existence and, looking sharply at

the visitor, would emphasise his points with frequent interjections—'wissen Sie, verstehen Sie' . . . (you know, you understand) . . . '*Das* ist die Sache!' (*That's* how it is) . . . 'Das ist
ganz einfach!' (you see, it's *very* simple). He would also often
tap the guest lightly on the arm or chest with the point of a
coloured pencil, with a test tube, a cigar or his thick-rimmed
spectacles which he frequently took off and swung about by
one of the strong side-pieces before putting them on again.
He stood with his head pushed forward a little, his gentle face
upraised to the visitor, who, as Ehrlich was a small man,
usually towered above him. With the wrinkles on his high forehead growing still deeper, he looked penetratingly at the other
person with his big bright eyes, in which from the depth of
his soul a world of kindliness was reflected. I loved to watch
such a scene as they gazed at each other, the visitor listening
intently, and Ehrlich gesticulating as though to hammer in
his meaning. It was a wonderful sight which could, I am sure,
inspire a painting or a statue personifying learning and elo-
quence.

Ehrlich's manner was friendly and jovial to all around him,
his fellow-workers, assistants and employees. New-comers, or
people whose work did not often bring them in contact with
the Chief, were, however, often a little embarrassed and
uneasy when they had to see him, in spite of his amiability.
This was partly because Ehrlich's exuberant manner made it
hard to grasp his meaning at first, and his directions were
always given with suggestions and allusions only. Also there
was a little imp in him which made him make joking remarks
with an absolutely serious face, and this, with his habit of
making fun of himself, confused some people who were not
used to it. Those who knew him well, however, could always
guess what he wanted from the slightest hint.

Ehrlich judged his fellow-workers and employees entirely by
their knowledge and ability and the work actually done, and
often thought it right to ignore weak points of character. He
said that the private life of those who worked with him did not
concern him providing they did their duty well, and he never
listened to gossip or scandal.

Very often he was able to form an opinion of the ability of
a man from a single scientific letter. In this way he often found

capable collaborators, and formed real friendships. A young Dr. Chem. (Doctor of Chemistry) who merely wrote him a letter about a scientific question—not asking for an appointment—soon became his assistant. At the beginning of the century, for instance, Ehrlich became convinced of the great significance of Professor R. Willstätter, the famous investigator of chlorophyll, plant pigments and enzymes, who was living at that time in Munich, after he had had some correspondence with him on scientific questions. Somewhat later, when his attention was called to the pioneering experiments to produce gamma-rays in Röntgen-tubes to replace radium which were being done by Professor Friedrich Dessauer, the great importance of this work was at once obvious to him, and he gave it all the encouragement he possibly could. He not only induced Professor Dessauer to make animal experiments in great numbers, but he also appealed to persons in authority for financial help to promote these investigations.

If an assistant's work was not up to the standard Ehrlich expected in the particular job he had given him—which did not mean he would not be quite capable in other fields of science—Ehrlich took care to see that another position was found for him, and in most cases this was of such advantage to the retiring assistant that he could only be thankful for the change. On the other hand, he would bestow unlimited encouragement on everyone who showed ability and did reliable work for him.

Ehrlich always liked independence and was glad if he did not have to look after all the little details of work. He wanted 'centralisation of investigation with independence of the individual worker'. He gave complete freedom in their special fields to Dr. Max Neisser and Dr. Hans Sachs, who had worked with him for a long time and in whom he had absolute confidence. Dr. Neisser became head of the Hygiene and Bacteriology Section, and Dr. Sachs of the Serology Section. He also gave a great deal of liberty to many of the other collaborators to work as they liked at their own particular jobs. When, however, he knew that an assistant liked to undertake on his independent initiative investigations which did not fit in with his own plans, Ehrlich could be extremely rigorous and strict, and was very angry if his instructions were not properly observed. He cnce severely reprimanded an assistant who had torn up one of the 'blocks' Ehrlich had sent him with instructions for his work, without having done the experiment. He evidently thought the Chief would forget about it, but Ehrlich always knew exactly what directions he had given. He would also look at the duplicate-book, and from time to time he sent reminders to those assistants who did not report on their work.

. . . . .

Ehrlich only sat at the desk in his study when he was reading scientific periodicals or books. It was so full there was no room to write on it. So when he wanted to write or dictate we went into the adjoining laboratory; but even there every available space, including the small writing-table, was often covered with piles of papers, and unless it was possible to move some of these—but he did not like to have *anything* moved, as we know—I had to take down my shorthand notes standing up.

Ehrlich believed in the following principles on work in general:

'Much testing; accuracy and precision in experiment; no guesswork or self-deception. Much working, but few publications; no "provisional" or "preliminary" reports.'

In contrast with these high standards, his requirements for working conditions were very modest.

'I can just as well work in a barn,' he often said, reminding his listener of the extremely primitive facilities he had had at Steglitz—just an old disused bakery and a stable—'and really only need test tubes, a Bunsen burner and blotting-paper,' he continued.

Dr. Ludwig Benda wrote the following description in his article in the book about Ehrlich's scientific work[1] which was dedicated to him in celebration of his sixtieth birthday:

'Coming into Ehrlich's laboratory we find to our great surprise that many things generally found in a laboratory are missing. In a medium-sized room stands an immense laboratory bench on which, closely packed together, are hundreds of small, some of them very small, bottles filled with different chemicals. It seems a hopeless chaos, but Ehrlich, having

---

[1] Paul Ehrlich, *Eine Darstellung seines wissenschaftlichen Wirkens Festschrift zum 60. Geburtstage des Forschers, 14 März, 1914* (Gustav Fischer, Jena 1914). S. 417/18.

arranged the substances according to a peculiar system of his
own, finds everything he looks for.

'From this ocean of bottles rises a single large Bunsen burner.
Close to it there is a small wooden box containing test tubes.
These, with some boards and shelves along the walls con-
taining the usual reagents and substances for making solutions,

A test tube experiment

complete the equipment of this laboratory, in which Ehrlich
works without any assistance. Here one would look in vain for
cylinders and retorts, funnels, beakers and jars, bowls and
basins, a refrigerator or thermometer, and all the vessels and
accessories which are the normal tools of the chemical worker.
Ehrlich has for years used only the test tube to make his
observations. This is sufficient for him to follow almost any
reaction to the point where he can judge the way it will turn
out. He is a virtuoso in the art of test tube experiments.'

.   .   .   .   .

As I entered the room where he did his writing, Ehrlich said
'Tag ook' and nodded kindly.

'Jetzt wollen wir mal schreiben . . .' (Now, let us write) he used to say and at once began dictating rapidly, pacing up and down the room with long strides 'like an impatient thoroughbred horse that cannot bear to go in a team and always wants to be off', as Felix Pinkus said.

In the middle of dictation Ehrlich sometimes said:

'E—i—nen Augenblick!' (Just a moment) and began searching for something among the glasses and bottles on the big bench. Not finding what he sought on the top, he opened the doors of the cupboards which formed the lower part of the laboratory bench which almost filled the room. This revealed shelves on which were still more bottles—innumerable they seemed—filled with rare and precious chemical substances. While searching he sat in a strange squatting position, with both knees drawn up equally high in an almost impossible position. It was difficult for him to keep his balance, and one would think that any moment he must fall over backwards. But so he remained for a full quarter of an hour, rummaging and searching and looking attentively at each bottle until he found what he was hunting for. He studied each bottle he took into his hand, turned it round, and observed with pleasure what was written on the label. Many a preparation which he had, perhaps, received a long time ago, thus came into his hand again, and reminded him of former experiments which now gave rise to a new flight of ideas.

All written work was forgotten for the time being, and he would begin experimenting. Test tube after test tube was taken out of the little box near the Bunsen burner, and minute quantities of various chemical compounds were put into them, solutions were made and heated, alkalis and acids added. Now a delightful violet-blue resulted from the experiment, then it was a bright red; now green, then orange. If he found an interesting reaction he called out:

'Wonderful! wonderful!' and showed it to me as though I understood all about it.

Then he would make the test on white blotting-paper, as already described. Dr. Benda forgot this simple but important accessory in his interesting picture of Ehrlich's laboratory.

We know the delight Ehrlich found in looking at the different colours, and the important conclusions he gathered from them.

There were also great numbers of wool and cotton threads, in every possible colour and shade from light to dark, which Dr. Benda sent in regularly and which also played a special rôle in these experiments.

Simpler and more primitive working conditions can hardly be imagined; and yet it was with these conditions that Ehrlich made all his important discoveries.

Benda wrote:

'When Ehrlich finds a reaction which seems to him sufficiently interesting to be followed up, he describes it to a friend or an assistant and then gives views on how it should be worked out.

'To work with Ehrlich is a real pleasure. The tenacity with which he holds on to an idea, seizes a problem and sticks to it until he has solved it, has a powerful effect upon his fellow-workers. His optimism which saves him from being down-hearted in cases of failure (with which every investigator must reckon) is transmitted to his pupils. How often, when a chemical preparation in which we had great confidence and hope proved to be too toxic, or insufficiently effective, did he encourage us, saying:

' "If we now introduce chlorine, or if we eliminate the sulphonating groups, we shall have what we want." And we took new courage, added chlorine, eliminated sulphonating groups, and—often attained what we wanted.

'The delight, also, that Ehrlich feels and shows in his beaming features when we bring him an exceptionally beautiful crystallised preparation, or a new dye with bright colouring, has an encouraging effect on his collaborators and stimulates them to new activity.

'Ehrlich is self-taught as a chemical investigator but he is "the born chemist". The happy union of the prominent biological and medical investigator, and the distinguished chemical worker, as we see it in Ehrlich and are unlikely to find it a second time, has turned out to the benefit of both disciplines, chemical and medical.'

When Ehrlich found some very interesting facts in his experimenting he would even let his cigar go out—which he would never otherwise do—and keep the cold cigar in his mouth, forgetting to relight it or to lay it aside. Even visitors. whom he usually liked to see, were unwelcome at that time.

If Kadereit announced someone at such a moment, Ehrlich shook himself unwillingly and complained:

'Another visitor—just when I am in the middle of my best work! Then he must wait!' he added quickly, and sometimes kept the visitor waiting so long that he went away. For Ehrlich forgot completely about him, and so completely did he lose all sense of time that he might be between one and a half and two hours before he remembered that there was someone waiting to see him. Calling Kadereit to show the visitor in he received the astonished and indignant answer:

'But he has gone long ago!'

'But why did you send him away?' said Ehrlich somewhat reprovingly. 'I told you that he should wait!'

To this Kadereit replied in self-defence:

'I did not send him away, he left of his own accord because you were so long.'

And all Ehrlich could say to this was:

'Oh, is it already *so* late? Well, then I shall go home.'

Sometimes, after leaving the Institute and stepping into the cab which always waited at the gate for him late in the afternoon, he would suddenly ask the coachman, when he had started, to stop again at the Georg Speyer-Haus. Descending in haste he would go up once more to the chemical laboratory there. In the short distance between the two institutes something had come into his mind which he must immediately speak about to one of his chemical workers.

In the middle of his experiments he sometimes said:

'Oh . . . er—please excuse me!' and was already out of the door, even in the worst kind of weather, without hat, without overcoat, even without his cigars, running over to the Speyer-Haus to tell his chemical assistants about a new reaction he had just found. It was useless to wait for him; it might be an hour or more before he came back, so I would go upstairs to my room and begin writing. Usually after a while I would hear his voice at the entrance of the building, calling out: 'Ka—de —reit!' and immediately afterwards: 'Markart!' (He always pronounced my name in the French way.) I hastened downstairs, and as I entered Ehrlich said:

'Al—so, was hatten wir zuletzt gesagt?' (Now then, what did we say last?)

And so the interrupted thread of dictation was taken up again—until the next interruption.

On less stormy afternoons, when there was no disturbance, Ehrlich attended to his experiments calmly, dictating at the same time. Often something else occurred to him which he did not want to forget. Without pausing in his work he went on speaking—but speaking about something quite different. Then, without quite finishing this, he would dictate a 'block'—notes for himself or one of his assistants. Then he suddenly came back to the first dictation which he had interrupted. There was no time to ask questions, and he did not like it. So I had to find out for myself how the different parts of the dictation fitted together and for whom they were intended.

If Ehrlich wanted to be alone for some time in order to work undisturbed he would ask me, after he had dictated several letters, or parts of them: 'How much have we now?' Knowing what he meant by this question, I said that I could type part of the letters straight away, to which he nodded agreement and said:

'If you will kindly do so . . .' without looking up from his experiments.

On one occasion Ehrlich did not want to interrupt the dictation for very long, but only to make a few little experiments. He asked me which of the letters were short so that I could type them at once. I mentioned some of the short letters, and he nodded. Then I also mentioned the letter to Professor Wechselmann of Berlin (who as one of the first dermatological specialists had taken an important part in trying Ehrlich's new preparations in human medicine). But I corrected this immediately and added:

'No, that letter is longer.'

Ehrlich was, however, already absorbed in his test tube experiments and merely repeated absent-mindedly:

'So—hm—yes—Wechselmann is longer—yes—— Wechselmann is longer——' Then raising his voice he looked at me for a second and nodded:

'Hm—yes—Wechselmann is longer!—yes—wenn Sie wollten so gut sein!' (if you will please do that).

I retired from the room very quickly. . . .

.   .   .   .   .   .

If a holiday were approaching it had to be announced beforehand, and this announcement had to be repeated several times, although generally it left him quite indifferent. On one occasion I said on a Monday:

'Thursday will be a holiday, Herr Geheimrat.'

Without stopping his experiment and without looking up, he asked:

'Ja, wieso denn . . . wieso denn?' (Well, how so, how is that?)

'Ascension Day, Herr Geheimrat,' I replied.

He went on shaking and heating the test tube, his whole attention absorbed by the developing reaction, and repeated:

'Wieso Ascension? Wieso Ascension. . . . Oh, a splendid reaction!'

If, however, a coming holiday displeased him and would disturb all his plans of work, there was always great excitement:

'Wieso denn? . . . wieso denn? . . . You ought to have told me *long* ago!'

'There is still plenty of time' I would say, trying to calm him, and then I reminded him every day of all the urgent letters and articles which must be attended to before this holiday came. But not until the very last day were these things dealt with, in great haste but with astonishing clearness and concentration: not only were recent letters answered, but also a lot of old ones which, it had seemed, would remain forgotten forever, even in the pigeon-hole marked 'urgent'.[1] Then, in the afternoon, perhaps an article of several pages or a long scientific letter would be written—'dashed off' so to speak. It looked as though the end of the world was coming, and Ehrlich thought he must make a complete clearance of all arrears before this happened.

---

[1] There was some correspondence about this 'pigeon-hole' (simply a wooden box with 'urgent' written on it) with Ehrlich's friend Prof. Kossel of Heidelberg, who had undertaken to do some experiments with a preparation Ehrlich had sent him. When asked about the result of his experiments, Prof. Kossel replied in a letter dated 2nd August: 'I wrote to you about it already last Spring but my letter seems to have got into the "pigeon-hole" for "urgent" matter, as I never received an answer to it and I felt very sad about it.' To this Ehrlich replied: (but not until 30 December in spite of several reminders from me) 'I had written on the "urgent" pigeon-hole: "New Year's Greetings for H. Kossel!" So you see this thing does not work so badly as you think it does!' And his friend was reconciled.

CHAPTER XIV

ATOXYL AND OTHER ARSENICALS

As has been seen, the systematic examination of chemical substances with relation to their curative powers was, in the first place, undertaken with dyes of the benzidine, triphenylmethane and acridine series, and with arsenical compounds. With regard to arsenical compounds, it was Ehrlich's most urgent task to open up this field of chemical research. At the beginning of the century extensive experiments with Atoxyl in the treatment of various diseases had been begun by a number of chemical investigators. Thomas and Breinl, in Liverpool, had found in 1906 that it had curative action in experimental trypanosomiasis, though Ehrlich and Shiga had not observed this with the strain of trypanosomes, relatively insensitive to arsenic, which they were using. But it had later been found to have a highly toxic effect on the optic nerve, and, because of the danger that a patient might become blind, treatment with Atoxyl had been practically abandoned. Its use in medicine seemed to have come to a dead end, because Atoxyl, according to its accepted chemical constitution, which was that of an anilide of arsenic acid, would have been chemically unreactive, yielding derivatives with great difficulty, if at all. For this reason nobody had thought of trying to make other such organic arsenical compounds for use in medicine.

Even before the Georg Speyer-Haus was built, Ehrlich had already found in his chemical experiments undertaken at the Serum Institute that Atoxyl had a chemical constitution entirely different from what had been described by Béchamp in

$$C_6H_5NH-As{\overset{\displaystyle OH}{\underset{\displaystyle OH}{=\!\!=\!\!=}}}O$$

1863, and ever since supposed to be correct. According to Béchamp, Atoxyl was a 'chemically indifferent anilide which could easily be split into its components'. Ehrlich, however, found that it was an amino-phenyl-arsenic acid, or arsanilic acid, and therefore a stable substance, and one from which derivatives could be made with great ease, on account of the

$$\text{NH}_2$$

As=O with OH and ONa

possession of a reactive, free amino-group. It was this discovery alone which made Atoxyl accessible to further chemical and biological development.

Not until months after this had been ascertained by Ehrlich himself did Dr. A. Bertheim, in accordance with a wish of Frau Speyer, the founder of the Georg Speyer-Haus, receive an invitation to work with him. He was immediately charged by Ehrlich with the task of working out in exact detail the indications which he had obtained regarding the real chemical constitution of Atoxyl. The first scientific communication on the subject was published jointly by Ehrlich and Bertheim on 1 May, 1907, as the first successful work issued by the Georg Speyer-Haus.

The background to this discovery was full of excitement for Ehrlich. As the internal fittings of the Speyer-Haus were not completely ready when he arrived, in the Spring of 1906, Dr. Bertheim had to commence his work at the Serum Institute, under conditions which might be called primitive for exact chemical work. As soon as everything was ready in the Georg Speyer-Haus, in the Summer of that year, he was able to continue his investigations there. Dr. von Braun was appointed head of the Chemical Section of this Institute.

Serious internal conflicts arose in the Speyer-Haus from this situation. His chemical collaborators and assistants refused to acknowledge that Ehrlich, whose doctrines were so different from those of all other chemical experts, was an authority in chemical matters, and they resisted his orders. These events took place in a very exciting way.

Ehrlich declared firmly to the three chemical workers at the Speyer-Haus:

'Atoxyl is *not* an anilide of arsenic acid. On the contrary, it contains a free amino-group; I have worked on the arsenic

Dr. Alfred Bertheim, Chemical Assistant at the Georg Speyer-Haus

azo-dyes, which can be made in consequence of this, for some considerable time.

'The necessity of reducing Atoxyl has been, *eo ipso*, the basis of my experiments, and I find hydrosulphite most appropriate for this purpose.

'In accordance with the biological facts I have deliberately asked for the most simple derivatives to be worked out first.

I must ask you to follow my orders strictly. You cannot judge whether this is right or not.'

To this Dr. von Braun answered:

'We cannot accept your directions, and must work according to the classic formula of Béchamp.'

Ehrlich, his voice raised, said sharply:

'I adhere to my orders and leave it to you to take the consequences.'

He turned his back on them and left the laboratory, raging inwardly. The three stood breathless, stupefied. Dr. von Braun took off his white overall and put on his overcoat.

'I am leaving,' he said.

Dr. Schmitz did the same. Dr. Bertheim waited a moment, motionless, reflecting. Then he said:

'Perhaps he is right, after all. I shall stay.'

The other two left the building. Dr. Schmitz soon afterwards began to work at the Physical Institute of the City of Frankfurt. Later on he had a leading position in one of the scientific institutes of Breslau. When, years after Ehrlich's death, a plaque to commemorate his birth was placed on the house where he was born at Strehlen (Silesia), it was Dr. Schmitz who started off the dedication of this memorial with a long and enthusiastic speech.

Ehrlich returned to his laboratory at the Serum Institute after this scene with his assistants, and was again at work when a few hours later Dr. Bertheim came into his room. He simply said:

'Herr Geheimrat. . . . I should like to stay with you.'

Ehrlich looked up at him momentarily and then, without stopping his experiment, nodded in a friendly way and said:

'All right, that's good.'

'I shall make the experiments you suggested this morning.'

'All right, my dear Bertheim.'

Ehrlich continued his work on the lines he intended, now faithfully assisted by Dr. Bertheim. The true constitution of Atoxyl was established, and the great increase of its potency with reduction of the arsenic to the trivalent, arsenious acid. One of the first advances with the aromatic arsenical compounds, in 1906, was the preparation of the sodium salt of acetyl-para-amino-phenyl-arsinic acid, called 'Arsacetin', which proved to be very effective against experimental try-panosomiasis. Then, still further progress produced 'Arseno-phenylglycin', No. 418 of these preparations, which had all been tried in numerous animal experiments. Tropical investi-gators unanimously agreed that this was the most powerful

Commemorative plaque on Ehrlich's birthplace

remedy which had till then been found against tropical diseases caused by trypanosomes.

Finally, Ehrlich arrived at his 606th preparation, the hydro-chloride of dioxy-diamino-arseno-benzene. This preparation

$$As\!=\!\!=\!\!As$$

NH$_2$ NH$_2$

OH   OH

606

could have been used for medical treatment some years earlier than it was, for by 1907 it had been worked out and a patent procured for it. However, when its action upon trypanosomes was tested in animal experiments, Ehrlich's assistant in the biological section of the Speyer-Haus at that time reported that he had not seen it produce any effect whatever on the infected animals which were treated with it, and so 606 was put aside. It is impossible to imagine how its activity was missed. One can only suppose that perhaps that assistant found No. 418 (Arsenophenylglycin) so effective that he did not trouble to make the animal experiments with 606 at all. Or it may be that he handled it only carelessly and superficially. At any rate, no result was at that time observed with it. Soon afterwards the assistant had to leave the Speyer-Haus because he disobeyed the rules of the Institute. Two years later Dr. Hata, a Japanese, came to work with Ehrlich. He was a pupil of Ehrlich's old friend Professor Kitasato of Tokio, and was sent by him to Ehrlich to work experimentally under his direction on syphilis in infected rabbits. It was not until Ehrlich asked him, soon after he arrived in 1909, to try all the arsenical compounds which he had worked out up till that time, making extensive therapeutic experiments, that the astonishing efficiency of 606 became evident. This will be reported later in detail.

. . . . .

One day in 1905, Dr. Sachs, from the Serological Section of the Serum Institute, had come rushing excitedly into Ehrlich's laboratory, in great contrast with his usual calm, quiet manner. His face was radiant, and he was waving with one hand a daily newspaper and with the other a copy of the latest *Wiener Klinische Wochenschrift*. He called out as he came:

'Herr Geheimrat—the microbe causing syphilis has been discovered!'

Ehrlich hurried to meet him, exclaiming with the greatest interest:

'Wieso denn, wieso denn?' (You don't say so!)

He took the newspaper and the *Wiener Klinische* and looked at them.

'Wunderbar!—Grossartig!!' (Miraculous! Magnificent!)

'Fritz Schaudinn of Vienna and Erich Hoffmann, both together at the Reichsgesundheitsamt in Berlin,' said Dr. Sachs, nodding with a smile. 'They say it's only a preliminary report, but surely it will soon be shown that they are right.'

Ehrlich looked up at Dr. Sachs, his great eyes gazing at him over his glasses, his head bent forward, the wrinkles on his forehead very deep. And with a little regret in his voice he said:

'And *not* Albertus magnus with his monkey experiments in

Professor Albert Neisser

Batavia! It is a pity—I should have liked him to have found it!'

But then he was overcome with joy at this important discovery, and hammering at Dr. Sachs with his coloured pencil in his ecstasy he shouted:

'But *now* . . . Grossartig!—It really *is* magnificent!'

One afternoon the following year, in the autumn of 1906, Kadereit came in and announced a visitor in a peculiar way he had, opening his mouth slightly and pulling down his upper lip so that his whole face seemed longer than it really was. He used this expression to indicate the importance of the visitor.

'Herr Jeheimrat,' he said with his Berlin accent, 'Professor Hoffmann of Bonn would like to see you.'

'What? Hoffmann?' said Ehrlich delightedly. 'That's marvellous—wunderbar! Tell Sachs to come . . .' and he went quickly to the door to greet Hoffmann, who was just entering. He had been appointed Professor in the meantime, left Berlin and taken charge of the Clinic for Dermatology at the University of Bonn.

'Tag ook, Herr Kollege,' said Ehrlich, 'this is a pleasant surprise, and a—l—s—o, wissen Sie, verstehen Sie, this wonderful discovery of yours . . .'

Then Dr. Sachs entered and as soon as both had greeted each other, Professor Hoffmann said brightly:

'I should have come long ago to see you about it, but then, the publications . . .'

'I know, I know, ja natürlich, natürlich, you have had a lot of work,' said Ehrlich, to which Hoffmann replied with a smile:

'Now that, after all the "Preliminary Reports" of last year, there is evidence that we *really have* the spirochaete of syphilis, I want to ask you to give me some of the preparations which you have found effective in animal experiments. I should like to try them out on syphilitic patients in my clinic, especially as the spirochaeta pallida of syphilis resembles somewhat the trypanosomes of relapsing fever and tropical diseases.'

'Ausgezeichnet . . . ausgezeichnet!' (excellent!) said Ehrlich, 'but be cautious, be careful, dear colleague.'

Professor Hoffmann nodded with a pleasant reassuring smile.

'Wissen Sie, verstehen Sie,' went on Ehrlich, 'we have had fine results with trypan-red, in animal experiments on trypanosomes, carried out by Dr. Shiga and Dr. Browning. You can look at Dr. Browning's animals over there,' and he made a sign in the direction of the Speyer-Haus.

Ehrlich was walking up and down the room as he spoke, and every time he passed Professor Hoffmann standing near the big laboratory bench he tapped at him with his coloured pencil or his glasses, which he kept taking on and off. Ehrlich had offered Hoffmann a glass of mineral water which was put on the table, and, as he passed to and fro, he always took a drink from his

Dr. Carl H. Browning of Glasgow, Ehrlich's Assistant in 1904–5

own glass, or from Professor Hoffmann's, indiscriminately. He also stopped occasionally to write down something—something that had nothing to do with what he was speaking about —a chemical formula, any scrawl or scribble, on the door of the bookcase at the left of the big door leading to the corridor. Finally he opened this door and called out for Kadereit. When

Kadereit came, Ehrlich just nodded and said, with a glance of
mutual understanding:

*The cupboard in Ehrlich's laboratory showing his scribbled notes.
On the right can be seen a bundle of coloured threads which
Ehrlich used in his experiments*

'Kadereit—"C".'

'Jawoll, Herr Jeheimrat,' replied Kadereit, quickly turning
his back and going out again. Ehrlich remarked to Hoffmann
with a whimsical little smile, and so that Kadereit could hear
him:

'You see, my dear Colleague, Kadereit even knows that! I do not need to say much to him. We understand each other by simply making a sign or saying a letter.'

There was general laughter, and Kadereit hurried away as fast as his already slightly stiff legs would carry him. He came back at once with a new box of cigars which he had opened, and handed it to Ehrlich. Ehrlich offered them to Dr. Hoffmann and Dr. Sachs and took one for himself. But none of them lit up at once, for Ehrlich went on speaking.

He went on speaking, still going up and down the room and round the big table to the window and back again; scribbling on the bookcase and the door, tapping both Hoffmann and Sachs—this time with the point of his cigar—and always talking, talking.

'Wissen Sie, verstehen Sie, in immunisation we have a really powerful weapon. What distinguishes *Serumtherapy* is that the protecting substances are products of the organism, and that they attack the parasites but not the organism itself. They are *parasitotropic*, but not *organotropic*. They are *"magic bullets" aiming only at the pernicious bodies strange to the organism, and striking only these and not the organism itself. Re vera*, Serumtherapy cannot be applied to all infectious diseases, especially those which are caused by protozoa, malaria, trypanosomes or spirilla. . . .'

Professor Hoffmann and Dr. Sachs nodded in agreement.

'Therefore,' went on Ehrlich, 'we *must* have *chemical substances and replace Serumtherapy with Chemotherapy*. This is certainly the case with syphilis.'

Professor Hoffmann agreed. Ehrlich was standing facing him, and obviously fascinating his taller colleague with his way of speaking, the power of his mind and spirit, the intensity of his will and his profound earnestness.

'We have made experiments,' Ehrlich went on, 'with substances obtained by reducing Atoxyl (arsanilic acid) and derivatives of the phenylarsinic acid; and we have convinced ourselves that not only the arsenic becomes fixed to the protoplasm, but that the other groups of the chemical molecule are also fixed in the same manner by specific receptors. There must therefore, *eo ipso*, exist more receptors in the cells. The chemical substance is, so to speak, fixed, with its different groups in succession, by special catching claws or traps of the protoplasm.

It is like a butterfly which is mounted by using different pins for all its parts. Just as a butterfly is first fixed with a pin through its trunk and then with others holding its wings, so does the fixation of the more complicated chemical substances take place.'

Professor Hoffmann, who, like Dr. Sachs, had followed Ehrlich's argument with the closest attention, said admiringly:

'The Side-Chain Theory in Chemotherapy. . . .'

But Ehrlich went on speaking:

'We must, of course, try out systematically *hundreds* of substances. Now we have Arsenophenylglycin—substance No. 418—which up to now is the most effective we have found. We must go on—go on! Come and see our experiments!'

He had already opened the door and went out, rushing forward, completely carried away by his ideas, always looking onward, onward.

The other two followed him. Dr. Sachs accompanied Professor Hoffmann to the steps leading out of the house, then bid him good-bye and went upstairs to his own section, while Professor Hoffmann hurried after Ehrlich. Conversing earnestly, they went over to the Speyer-Haus. Ehrlich was balancing his spectacles and waving them about and up and down, saying:

'What is present in my mind is the idea of a therapia sterilisans magna—curing and healing at one blow. That *must* be attainable! We must not squander time and delay treatment by using too small doses. If it has once been established, through countless animal experiments and trials on human patients, that a certain chemical substance is *well tolerated*, then *strong* doses must be given according to the old maxim "frapper fort et frapper vite".'

Having arrived at the Georg Speyer-Haus they went into the Biological Sections, where Ehrlich showed his visitor the record books of the animal experiments and also the animals themselves. Then they went upstairs into the Chemical Section, where Dr. Kahn (who had replaced Dr. von Braun) and Dr. Bertheim, Dr. Bauer and the laboratory assistants were all busily at work. Ehrlich having introduced Professor Hoffmann, said firmly to Dr. Bertheim:

'Dear Dr. Bertheim, we must absolutely eliminate oxygen in

preparing the substances, and bottle them in a vacuum in order to avoid oxidation. Please think over how this can best be done, and give me your report. This is absolutely necessary.'

. . . . .

Meanwhile Kadereit had gone into Ehrlich's laboratory at the Serum Institute to clear up the room. He picked up all the cigar stumps, the half-smoked cigars and the cut-off ends about which Ehrlich was always rather extravagant. As his master smoked at least twenty-five a day there were quite a lot to gather up. Kadereit savoured the fragrance, relishing in advance the pleasure he would have when he filled his pipe on Sunday with the finely cut, precious tobacco.

When Ehrlich came back to the Serum Institute after Professor Hoffmann had gone, he saw that Männe his dachshund was in the garden. Poor Männe was very ill, he had a sarcoma, and the growth caused him great pain. He could no longer walk much, and so had to stay with Kadereit, instead of escorting his master home. This made him so ill-humoured that he did not want to have anything more to do with Ehrlich, and ran away when he saw him. Ehrlich called to him several times:

'Come, Männe, come . . .' but the dog paid no attention and went up the steps into the house as quickly as he could and scratched at Kadereit's door. Kadereit opened it and said to Ehrlich, who was once more calling the dog, sadly:

'He is not well, Herr Jeheimrat.'

Ehrlich nodded sorrowfully. 'He is offended, because he is not allowed to accompany me,' he said. 'But it is not possible any longer. Soon'—and Ehrlich turned his back on Kadereit so as not to let him see his emotion—'soon we shall have to part with him.' And he went slowly, deep in thought, into his laboratory.

Before his illness Männe used always to jump first into the carriage that was waiting outside and jump out first when they arrived. Ehrlich often gave a lift to one of his assistants, who always got out at the railway station. Ehrlich used to tease the dog by opening the door on the right to let the assistant out. The dog wanted to get out too, but always scratched at the left-hand door of the cab, the side facing the station buildings, and only wanted to get out that way. Probably some association in connection with travelling was present in the dog's mind.

But this stubbornness on the part of his pet always amused
Ehrlich greatly.

.   .   .   .   .   .

More Resistance

The next morning Kadereit as usual returned to the Institutes from Ehrlich's home with a pile of letters and 'blocks.'
He hurried up the stairs in the Georg Speyer-Haus and handed
a 'block' each to Dr. Kahn, Dr. Bertheim and Dr. Bauer, and
then went down to the Biological Section to distribute the
other mail.

Dr. Kahn and Dr. Bauer read their 'blocks' and put them
on their benches. Dr. Bertheim merely glanced at his and
then, with an angry expression on his face, tore it up into
little pieces and put it in one of the high jars used for rubbish.

When, shortly after this, Ehrlich came into the Chemical
Section, they were all busily at work. He was, as always, except
in winter, bareheaded and had his cigar-box pressed under his
left arm. He greeted them all in his usual kind manner and
then, turning to Dr. Kahn, asked:

'Was gibts Neues?' (Is there anything new?)

Dr. Kahn showed him some experiment, they spoke together
in an undertone, Ehrlich nodded his consent and then said to
Dr. Bertheim:

'My dear Bertheim, have you already found out the dis-
pcsition?'

Dr. Bertheim, scarcely looking up from his work, answered
sullenly:

'What disposition, Herr Geheimrat?'

'What I told you yesterday,' said Ehrlich impatiently, 'that
the preparations must be protected by excluding oxygen.'

'No,' said Bertheim.

'I have also written you a "block" about it!' added Ehrlich
sharply.

Dr. Bertheim shrugged his shoulders obstinately without
stopping his work, and said nothing.

'Where is that "block" Dr. Bertheim?' demanded Ehrlich,
in a harsh tone. He was very angry.

Dr. Bertheim now interrupted his work and answered,
grumbling:

'I have torn it up.'

At this Ehrlich exploded with rage in a way he only did on very rare occasions. He called out to one of the laboratory boys:

'Tell Kadereit to come here *immediately* with the duplicate-book.'

The boy was shaking with fright and almost fell down the stairs in his haste. Instantly Kadereit came hurrying up with the duplicate-book.

Meanwhile Ehrlich had been striding to and fro in the laboratory, with clenched fists, his arms thrust backwards, his face hot with rage. He shouted out, with a bitterness and violence he never otherwise showed:

'Impudence! I do not give my directions for fun! If I give an order, it is *urgently necessary*! And I expect it to be carried out!'

Kadereit handed him the duplicate-book. Ehrlich opened it, turned over a few leaves until he came to the page on which the 'block' was copied, and slapped his hand violently down upon it. Dr. Kahn had come near him to look, and Ehrlich, pointing to the page, said excitedly:

'Dr. Kahn, I ask you to take note of this matter. If my instructions are not attended to—if we do not protect our preparations by the absolute exclusion of oxygen and bottle them in a vacuum'—Ehrlich got more and more excited as he spoke—'deaths will occur,' he continued, 'and the preparations will have to be thrown upon the dung hill! With oxidised preparations the greatest imaginable damage would be done! Please note the contents of the "block" and let me know *this very day* what you propose to do!'

Then he left the laboratory, still in a rage. Dr. Kahn made a copy of the 'block' from the duplicate-book, while Kadereit stood waiting beside him until he had finished. Dr. Bertheim, with a burning face, went sullenly back to his work.

With little faults and failures Ehrlich was always very indulgent, as is shown by several incidents, but he could be very stern whenever important questions were at stake. And this really was very important. If the preparations were not protected against oxygen, as he demanded, many would have been spoiled and would not have been fit to be used even in animal experiments, not to mention the treatment of human patients.

There would, at least, have been a serious hold up in the animal experiments, and no advance in clinical work, even if nothing worse happened.

.   .   .   .   .

One might well be astonished and ask how it was possible that Dr. Bertheim, after the scene over the constitution of Atoxyl when Dr. von Braun and Dr. Schmitz left, and he, Bertheim, had expressed his willingness to do his best in collaboration with Ehrlich, could now show such stubbornness and resistance to Ehrlich's directions. Perhaps there was a psychological reason for his behaviour. It may have been because he felt deeply hurt at having been put under Dr. Kahn, after Dr. von Braun left, and so having to approach Ehrlich through him, at least in secondary questions, instead of dealing always with Ehrlich direct. Dr. Kahn was in no way more able than Bertheim and proved a failure soon after, so that he had to leave. This will be explained later on. It could not, of course, have been foreseen.

.   .   .   .   .

Having returned to his own laboratory, Ehrlich smoked angrily, still scolding aloud:
'The impudence! Shameless! Such an incapable stubborn blockhead!'
Impatiently he tore open the drawers of his desk and took out some papers. Looking at them he noticed that mice had been eating them. Still in a passion he went on repeating:
'Impertinence! Shamelessness! *Caput pigerrimum*, incapable fellow!'
With the papers still in his hand he went to the door and called for Kadereit. Kadereit came running, and when he arrived, Ehrlich was already a little calmer. He never made other people suffer for his ill-humour.
'Kadereit, there are mice in the drawers here,' he said. 'You must order immediately tin boxes with tightly closing lids to fit exactly into the drawers—otherwise everything here will be eaten.'
Kadereit dared not say anything but: 'Certainly, Herr Jeheimrat,' and left the room again. He thought by himself that he might just as well have set mouse-traps, as is usually

done in such cases; but his master had demanded it that way, so that way it must be done without fail.

After tin boxes had been put in, the documents and writings inside were safe, but the little rodents were still free to carry on their mischief outside, without restrictions. The old sofa offered them especially good opportunities of amusing themselves among the high piles of books and manuscripts.

CHAPTER XV

PERSONAL CHARACTERISTICS AND THE NOBEL PRIZE

THE increased strain on his physical and mental powers, and the annoyance of the daily struggle to see that his orders were carried out, made Ehrlich need all the more some sort of recreation or simple amusement to rest his mind and calm his nerves. But there was now hardly any time for recreation. He used formerly to watch each morning the little green frog in his glass-house at home. Its behaviour gave him an opportunity of making jokes about the weather forecast. Now only a brief look at the frog, for a moment, was possible. But Ehrlich never forgot that Kadereit must bring food for the little amphibian, and even on Sundays, when he came to the house, Ehrlich's first question was always whether he had remembered the big test tube filled with flies which he had first to catch in the stables of the Institute.

Ehrlich was fond of animals and loved to watch them. In his autobiographical notes he calls himself a 'friend of animals'. A striking example of his knowledge of the peculiarities of animals is a story Sir Almroth Wright told me.

Once, when Ehrlich was talking with friends about his work of finding and setting up a standard for the effective strength of diphtheria antitoxin, they asked him how it was possible easily to give a horse the great number of injections necessary to obtain a very strong serum for diphtheria prophylaxis. Ehrlich answered:

'One must love the horse . . . and *ask* him!'

He had a great liking for all the small things in Nature. He preferred a simple, quiet landscape to an imposing range of mountains. From his favourite place on the little terrace of his home, where he liked to work quietly and undisturbed, he used to watch, day by day, in Springtime and Summer, a tiny mountain ash which had rooted upon the dying trunk of a poplar tree. The way this little seedling went on growing caused him real pleasure. Every insect, every bird, stirred his interest and attention.

> 'It's just the least, the quietest,
> The rustling of a lizard,
> A breath, a hush,
> The twinkling of an eye—
> Such small things make real happiness,'

he liked to quote from Nietzsche. It shows his modest, unpretentious happy nature, desirous of giving happiness to others, which was most fully expressed in his social life at home. He preferred to have only one guest at a time, to whom he could give his undivided attention.

Sometimes, when surrounded by a small circle of friends, he would make jokes and say outrageous things which he knew to be absurd, just to tease them; as when he amazed his guests with tales about 'American Lords' who do not exist in the U.S.A.

Martha Schiff, a friend of the family, said about him:[1]

'Until the very end of his life he would make little jokes which he himself enjoyed and which only those who knew him well could understand.'

She goes on to say that one Spring afternoon some weeks before his death he saw some friends in his library at home. They were talking about Weimar, where one of the visitors had just passed a few delightful days. Everyone had some pleasant recollection or special impression to tell of the place; and when one of them said:

'The most beautiful thing at Weimar is really the Shakespeare monument,' there followed a moment of silence. But Ehrlich interrupted this by saying, apparently quite seriously:

'That is only right and proper, as Shakespeare was born at Weimar.'

His wife, fearing for his reputation for general knowledge, said reproachfully:

'But Paul!'

Ehrlich, however, looked quite innocent, and it would have greatly amused him to make his friends think he was quite ignorant on this subject. But one of the friends saw the joke and took it up, and a lively conversation followed between

[1] *Deutsche Rundschau*, June, 1916.

him and Ehrlich, in which Shakespeare's cradle was transferred to Weimar and the house where he was born at Stratford-on-Avon was dismissed as a 'fairy-tale'.

Occasionally when guests were invited to dinner, Ehrlich tried to persuade his wife to have only foreign dishes served, and laughingly refused to believe that the guests would not like it.

.   .   .   .   .

I had been working for Ehrlich for several years before I knew that he was a Jew. He would never have thought of changing his religion for the sake of deriving any advantage by so doing, but he paid very little attention to the Jewish holidays and rites. He was, body and soul, entirely given up to science and research. His whole life was so deeply rooted in this world of his own that he was, as he himself said 'an outsider in religion, politics and other matters'. Yet he knew all about the actual events of the day. He had keen and sound opinions on many political questions, although he said that he was 'non-political' and that in every brain there was only a limited space which, in his own, was completely filled with chemistry, medicine and some mathematics. He only once went to vote. That was in January 1906, during the war in South-west Africa. But he was such an 'outsider' in the political world and the noisy bustle of elections that Kadereit had to go with him and explain to him how voting was done.

.   .   .   .   .

The Nobel Prize

In 1908 the papers bore the news that 'the well-known scientific investigator Professor Paul Ehrlich of Frankfurt-on-Main, and Professor Metchnikoff of the Pasteur Institute in Paris, have been awarded the Nobel Prize for Medicine for the year 1908 on account of their successful studies in Immunity'.

When Ehrlich went to Stockholm for a few days in order to receive the prize, attend the impressive ceremonies connected with its presentation and deliver his lecture before the Nobel Committee—which was done on 11 December—a newspaper reporter came to see him at his hotel and asked for an interview. He was received kindly by Ehrlich and asked him many questions, mainly on philosophy. Ehrlich courteously tried to make intelligible to him the inner relationship existing between philosophy and medicine. But finally the reporter, surprised by Ehrlich's repeated endeavours to switch over from philosophy to medicine, ventured to ask whether or not he had the honour of speaking to Professor Eucken of Jena (Professor of Philosophy, who was also a Nobel Prizewinner of 1908).

'Oh no,' replied Ehrlich with a smile, obviously relieved and taking a deep breath. 'No, I have not yet got as far as that, I am afraid you will have to go next door, please.'

The two laureates, Ehrlich and Eucken, had been given rooms next to each other in the same hotel and the reporter had mistaken the rooms.

Professor Sundberg, a member of the Nobel Committee, wrote to me some time ago giving the following account of Ehrlich's visit to Stockholm:

When he arrived he was met at the station by Professor

Ehrlich aged fifty-four

Sundberg, who asked him for the ticket for his luggage so that it could be claimed and looked after properly. Noticing that Ehrlich was holding two cigar-boxes tightly pressed under his left arm he wanted to take them from him; but Ehrlich laughingly protested at this, saying:

'Take everything else, but not my cigars! Really good cigars they are!'

Fearing that he would not be able to find the right kind of cigars in Stockholm he had taken a supply of his particular brand with him.

It is said that whenever a cigar was offered to Ehrlich he

generally took one out of politeness, but always contrived to slip it into his pocket at the first opportunity and replace it with one of his own.

When he returned to Frankfurt, Ehrlich's friends organised a party to celebrate the great honour bestowed upon him. Ehrlich did not like big official ceremonies, and for this reason his friends, who knew of this dislike, arranged a party on the lines of a students' reunion, in a big hall in Frankfurt— a beer party which was attended with much mirth and informal gaiety. Ladies were not admitted, but Ehrlich's wife and daughters, and those of his friends, were allowed to look on from the galleries above.

Dr. Adickes, the Lord Mayor of Frankfurt, made an enthusiastic speech in which he said he believed that Ehrlich would be capable, if required, of working at and managing any number of institutes for research besides the two he already had! The audience was quite carried away by this speech and showed its approval by much applause. It was Dr. Adickes who had, in collaboration with Dr. Althoff the Director in the Prussian Ministry in Berlin, first made it possible for Ehrlich to come to Frankfurt ten years previously.

CHAPTER XVI

606

Dr. ARTHUR VON WEINBERG had for many years been a friend of Ehrlich and had always greatly helped to promote his work. He was Director of the Cassella Chemical Works at Mainkur near Frankfurt, which were later on, as already mentioned, incorporated in the I.G. Farben Company. At the works he instructed Dr. Ludwig Benda to carry out chemical experiments almost exclusively for Ehrlich. Dr. Benda remained an external collaborator, even after the Georg Speyer-Haus was opened. He carried on an extensive correspondence with Ehrlich and often came to see him personally in order to talk to him about his experiments.

All the new chemical substances received from Dr. Benda (especially the trypan-dyes), as well as those worked out in the Speyer-Haus and largely derived from reduced Atoxyl (arsanilic acid) and its reduction products were tested for activity and toxic action in long series of experiments on white mice. Ehrlich gave daily instructions for these experiments and controlled what was going on. He worked unceasingly, made experiment after experiment, to find more preparations worth testing, and gave his collaborators information about all the important observations he made as a result of his test tube experiments, so that they could work them out according to exact chemical principles.

Working on these lines he had, as already stated, reached his 606th preparation in 1907. This preparation had been patented but afterwards put aside, as the assistant then working in the Biological Section of the Speyer-Haus reported that it had no effect when used in animal experiments, and that the 418th preparation, Arsenophenylglycin, was better.

In the Spring of 1909 Ehrlich's friend, Professor Kitasato of Tokio, sent a second pupil, Dr. Hata, to Europe to study with Ehrlich at the Speyer-Haus. After the news of the discovery of the spirochaete of syphilis by Professors Schaudinn and Hoffmann in 1905, Dr. Hata had begun working on experiments to produce syphilis in rabbits by inoculation, at the Kitasato Institute for Infectious Diseases in Tokio. He became very skilled in this work, and it was therefore natural that he should continue on these lines at the Speyer-Haus, producing infections in rabbits experimentally and then examining the preparations worked by Ehrlich and testing their curative properties on these infected animals. He was also charged with supervising their general care and treatment; and he carried out all his experiments exactly as Ehrlich advised, trying out all the preparations. Nor did he shirk repeating the experiments again and again, until a clear and definite result was obtained.

No outsider can ever realise the amount of work involved in these long series of animal experiments, with treatments that had to be repeated and repeated for months on end. No one can grasp what meticulous care, what expenditure and amount of time were involved. To get some idea of it we must bear in mind that Arsenophenylglycin had the number 418, Salvarsan the number 606. This meant that these two substances were the 418th and 606th of the preparations which Ehrlich worked out. People often, when writing or speaking about Ehrlich's work, refer to 606 as the 606th *experiment* that Ehrlich made. This is not correct, for 606 is the number of the *substance* with which, as with all the previous ones, very numerous animal experiments were made. The amount of detailed work which all this involved is beyond imagination.

Details of these events (Dr. Hata's arrival and work with Ehrlich) may interest the reader.

On a Spring day in 1909 Kadereit announced to his master: 'Dr. Hata has come.'

'Show him in,' said Ehrlich.

Dr. Hata entered the room with a deep bow, and was greeted by Ehrlich:

'Tag ook, dear Dr. Hata. I am very glad to see you. My friend Kitasato has written very well of you to me.'

Dr. Hata bowed again, with a happy smile, and said, emphasising each word with nods and movements of his head:

'Much pleased I'—pointing to himself—'to be allowed to work with Herr Professor Ehrlich.'

'My friend Kitasato tells me,' went on Ehrlich, making
gestures with his hand and speaking more slowly than usual to
help Dr. Hata to understand, 'he tells me that after the discovery of the spirochaete of syphilis by Schaudinn and Hoffmann you began at once to produce syphilis experimentally

Ehrlich with Dr. Hata

in rabbits by means of inoculations, and that you have acquired
great skill in doing this.'

'Very important, Herr Professor, very important,' answered
Dr. Hata with a polite bow.

'Ja, natürlich, natürlich' (yes, indeed, indeed), said Ehrlich.
'I would like you to continue with this work here. Make long
series of experiments,' he stretched out his arms wide, 'many

rabbits, and then try out all our old and new preparations one by one, thoroughly—very thoroughly!'

'Very happy, Herr Professor.' Dr. Hata's face was radiant, and he bowed incessantly. Ehrlich handed him a number of small bottles containing preparations, and pointed to the labels:

'Exact records—exact observations—and a report to come to me every day.'

Dr. Hata nodded, took the small bottles, looked attentively at the inscriptions on the labels and said proudly:

' 418 . . . 606 . . .'

'Come with me, Dr. Hata,' said Ehrlich. 'We will now go over to the Speyer-Haus. I will show you where you are to work and introduce you to the others. Over there'—he jerked his head in the direction of the Speyer-Haus—'we have still more preparations—many, many more. And,' he added, with a kind little laugh and a gesture of the hand, 'also much work, *everything* to be tried out!'

Dr. Hata was delighted. '*So* happy, Herr Professor,' he said.

.   .   .   .   .

Ehrlich was again occupied with experiments in his laboratory when Fräulein Krüger, a laboratory assistant, came in with a laboratory boy, who held in his hand a small cage containing a dead mouse. Without looking up from his work, Ehrlich asked:

'Tag ook . . . was gibts Neues?' (Is there anything new?)

Fräulein Krüger pointed to the dead mouse, saying:

'The feeding experiments, Herr Geheimrat . . . the others are still alive . . . what shall be done with this?'

Ehrlich looked up for a second, nodded to Fräulein Krüger and said briefly as he went on with his experiment:

'Fraschen. . . .' (This was his hasty pronunciation of 'Veraschen', i.e., incinerate.)

She stood there puzzled, but dared not ask what he meant, merely saying timidly as she left the room with the boy:

'Yes, Herr Geheimrat . . .'

She was very scared and had not the courage to ask one of the assistants. She did not often come in contact with the chief, and was one of those people (as she confessed to me later) who could not easily get used to Ehrlich's peculiar way of speaking. She stood bewildered in the room where she worked, and walked up and down repeating desperately:

'Fraschen . . . fraschen . . . what *did* he mean by that?'

The laboratory boy, who was a bright lad and full of common sense—a typical 'Frankfurt kid'—at length said:

'Och—perhaps he meant veraschen' (reduce it to ashes).

'Oh yes,' said Fräulein Krüger, much relieved. 'But how must that be done—veraschen—do you know?'

'Och,' replied the boy, 'maybe roasted, so that the mouse is burnt to ashes on a hot iron plate.'

So they proceeded to do this. It took a terribly long time, and the smell was dreadful. Now and then someone would want to enter the room, but as soon as the door was opened it was immediately closed again with a bang. Again and again Fräulein Krüger asked:

'I wonder if it *really* should be done this way?'

The next day Fräulein Krüger brought the iron plate with the poor remnants of the mouse's ashes. Ehrlich came close to look at it curiously.

'Tag ook,' he said. 'What fine thing have you got there?' (Was haben Sie Schönes?)

'Good morning, Herr Geheimrat,' said Fräulein Krüger. 'That is the—the—the mouse, burnt to ashes . . .' Her face was scared and her voice trembling.

Ehrlich gave her a curious inquiring look, but remained quite serious.

'So, yes, the mouse reduced to ashes . . . well . . . yes . . . I am sorry . . . there is nothing to be done about it!'

It seemed as if he wanted to comfort her; and so, suddenly conscious that she had done a very stupid thing, she withdrew hurriedly. She was amazed at such kindness and the absence of any reproach.

.   .   .   .   .   .

Death of Männe

Ehrlich's light-brown dachshund Männe was very ill—his illness had become so much worse that he had to be put to sleep.

Outside the half-open door of Kadereit's room, Dr. Max Neisser and Dr. Sachs stood waiting. Ehrlich came out of his own room, and the dog came out of Kadereit's. Previously, during his illness, Männe had avoided his master, but now he went to him and scratched at his feet, looking up imploringly as if to say:

'Help me—*you* must help me!'

Ehrlich, deeply touched, bent down to caress him, saying: 'Poor Männe . . .'

Dr. Sachs whispered to Ehrlich, trying to help him overcome his emotion, asking: 'Chloroform?'

Ehrlich nodded his assent. Dr. Neisser and Dr. Sachs went into the room, and Ehrlich went after them. The dog, sensing that something was going to happen, refused to follow. But finally he responded, though still reluctantly, to Ehrlich's call, and the door closed behind him.

.   .   .   .   .

Dr. Hata's First Observations

Having made his first experiments Dr. Hata came to show Ehrlich his records and said, with his usual polite bows:

'Only first trials—only preliminary general view.'

Ehrlich turned the leaves of the book and looked at the records. Satisfied, he nodded kindly and said:

'Very nice . . . very nice.'

He turned some more pages and found the last experiment made. Dr. Hata remarked:

'Believe 606 *very* efficacious . . .'

Ehrlich looked at the records and said, much astonished:

'No, surely not? Wieso denn . . . wieso denn? It was all minutely tested by Dr. R., and *he* found nothing—nothing!'

Ehrlich became very excited as he went on:

'It should have shown some effect then too . . . but he saw nothing! Saw nothing, the incapable *good-for-nothing!*'

Then looking at Dr. Hata, he continued, with an emphatic gesture:

'More than a year ago we laid aside 606 as being ineffective, worthless. You are sure you are not mistaken, Dr. Hata?'

Hata pointed to the records of the experiments and said, shrugging his shoulders:

'I found *that*, Herr Geheimrat.'

'Then it must be repeated, dear Hata, repeated,' said Ehrlich. 'To be sure of what we find there must always be many—innumerable—controls and repetitions. That must be the basis of our work.'

He looked happily at Dr. Hata, who bowed and left the room. Quite disturbed and excited, Ehrlich walked up and down the room, talking to himself:

'I *always* had a strong feeling—have been convinced for two years—*that* 606 *must be good!*'

.   .   .   .   .

In Ehrlich's study the pile of books, manuscripts and such like on the old sofa, the desk and the chairs, had grown so high that they towered above the high back of the sofa, and there was no space at all to write at the desk or sit on the chairs. It was no longer possible to put these piles under the sofa when important visitors came. The walls above and beside the sofa were becoming more and more covered with pictures up to the ceiling. Besides the old diagrams of the side-chain theory and the production of antitoxins in the infected body, there were new photographs of animal experiments made by Dr. Hata: pictures of chickens, white mice, rabbits, showing the progressive process of healing from spirochaetal infections with 418 and 606, from sickness to final recovery, drawings of curves and tables with endless numbers. These were mounted and framed with narrow oak frames. Filling every free space on the opposite wall were overcrowded bookcases, shelves carrying small bottles of chemical substances, envelopes yellowed with age containing some specially precious things which Ehrlich had put there for safety, and empty cigar-boxes which were used for storing microscopical preparations. In the corner to the left of the big window was a large calendar, a wooden plaque, 16×11 inches in size, with figures 7 inches high to show the date, as though Ehrlich could not be too strongly reminded of the flight of time. In spite of this, however, he never knew the date.

In view of Ehrlich's liking for accompanying his explanations with diagrams and drawings on any handy surface, it can be understood that both doors of his rooms, as well as the bookcases and any vacant space on the big laboratory bench, were all covered with chemical formulae and diagrams illustrating scientific hypotheses, side-chains, etc. It was a peculiar, fantastic world in which Ehrlich lived and worked: a world of his own.

When he received his pay from the Ministry, which was sent every three months in advance, he held the notes in his hands and counted them hastily. He took some of them and put them in his pocket-book, which he then returned to the inner pocket of his coat. Some he gave to Kadereit to pay at least part of the last bill from the firm of Wetzlar, which supplied his cigars. Then he took a book from the piles on the sofa—any book—hid the rest of the money in it and put it back in the same place. When he needed the money, he would be able with absolute certainty to find that particular book.

.   .   .   .   .

'A—l—s—o' (Now then . . .) said Ehrlich one day at the end of a long dictation, 'to whom have we written about 606?'

I had had to take this down standing up, note-book in hand, because, as always, there was no room anywhere to sit and write.

After the first positive findings of Dr. Hata about 606, all Ehrlich's outside collaborators, who had already been treating human diseases with 418 with good results, had to receive 606 for trial treatment, with exact instructions regarding its dosage and application. I read out the names:

'Professor Alt, Uchtspringe, Dr. Schreiber, Magdeburg, Professor Iversen, Petersburg, Professor Ascoli, Catania. . . .'

'And add Hoffmann, Bonn,' said Ehrlich. 'That will do for a beginning. Now . . . just a moment . . .'

He was off again, heating and shaking something over the flame.

Dr. Kahn from the Chemical Section of the Georg Speyer-Haus came over to see Ehrlich, who went a few steps to meet him. Dr. Kahn whispered something to Ehrlich, who listened attentively, and then replied with an angry gesture and a frown:

'Oh, let him criticise . . .'

When Dr. Kahn had gone, he turned to me, shaking himself as though to get rid of some irritating nuisance.

'Did you ever meet an assistant who does *not* grumble about his chief?' he said. 'I never did!'

Then he suddenly asked me:

'How long have we been together?'

'Almost eight years, Herr Geheimrat,' I replied.

'Really? As long as that already?' Then after a short pause in which he looked intently at me over his spectacles, he added:

'We have always got on well together, have we not?'

With all my heart I agreed.

'*Always*, Herr Geheimrat!' I said, smiling, and he nodded kindly.

．　　．　　．　　．　　．

Dr. Franke 'Had a Monkey' (*Franke hatte einen Affen*)

During the time he had worked with Ehrlich, Dr. Franke had made a great many experiments with trypanocidal dyestuffs. Among these were some in which he had treated a monkey infected with the trypanosome of sleeping-sickness. At length his time with Ehrlich had come to an end, he had left the Institute and returned to Silesia, where there were good opportunities for work in veterinary medicine. His successor was Dr. Boehme, who came from Kiel. Even after Dr. Boehme had been over six months at the Institute and in daily contact with Ehrlich, the latter still kept on calling him Dr. Franke, from habit.

One day Ehrlich wanted to dictate a lecture in which he was going to mention the experiments of Dr. Franke. Without stopping his usual work over the Bunsen burner, or looking up from his mixture, he began:

'A-l-s-o . . . now . . . we shall write . . . Franke had a monkey.'

In German this is 'Franke hatte einen Affen', and in German slang 'hatte einen Affen' means 'was tipsy'.

I ventured to laugh and interrupt Ehrlich, saying:

'But Herr Geheimrat, we cannot say it *that* way!'

'Wieso denn . . . wieso denn?' replied Ehrlich wondering; but without waiting for an answer or interrupting his work at all he began again:

'A-l-s-o, when Franke had a monkey . . .'

Again, I tried to make him change the expression:

'Herr Geheimrat, it really isn't possible to say that!'

But he was so deeply absorbed in his work that he did not appreciate the joke. A second's silence followed before he went on again as before:

'Hm . . . a-l-s-o . . . *damals* als Franke einen Affen hatte' (well . . . *at the time* when Franke had a monkey . . .)

There seemed no hope of sparing Dr. Franke the accusation of having been tipsy at least once in his life; of having had, as we say in German, 'einen Affen'. So I went on writing and changed the first sentence later when typing from my short-hand notes.

It may interest the reader to know what had become of Dr. Franke's monkey. This little animal, experimentally infected with trypanosomes and seriously ill with sleeping-sickness, had been completely cured with the dye-preparation known as trypan-red. It enjoyed the best of health, but had to be kept under observation for a long time because of the strong probability of a relapse later, which frequently occurs in sleeping-sickness. It felt so well, however, that in its high spirits it was given to all sorts of mischief, playing with test tubes, putting on Ehrlich's thick-rimmed spectacles, copying his ways and manners, and such like. One day it escaped from its cage, climbed up on to the roof of the stables, threw stones and dirt at the children of the staff, whose families lived at the Institutes, and frightened the patients resting in the gardens of the City Hospital at the back of the Ehrlich Institute. Finally, to put an end to this, the monkey had to be transferred to the Zoological Gardens. There it could play undisturbed and, to the amusement of the visitors, indulge in as much mischief as it liked.

606 *Really is Efficacious*

The curative treatments with 606 had amazingly successful results, but Ehrlich demanded that they should be repeated over and over again with hundreds and hundreds of experimentally infected animals, so that there could not possibly be any error. Even that tireless worker, Dr. Hata, began to get impatient. And that meant a great deal, for Ehrlich always spoke very highly of the untiring patience of the Japanese scientific investigators, who devoted enormous care to the

most insignificant details of experimental work, in spite of
the high standard of their scientific education and outlook.

Kadereit's portfolio, containing the letters and the long
reports which came in daily from the different clinics where
606 was first being tested on human patients, grew thicker
every day. When he came from Ehrlich's house, Kadereit
emptied his big leather bag on to the long, narrow laboratory
bench which stood under the windows. On the left-hand side
of this bench piles of papers were accumulating, as well as
everywhere else.

The whole work went forward, developing, not without
dramatic moments, to its culminating point. At length Ehrlich
convinced himself of the outstanding curative power of 606.
One morning he came quickly into his laboratory, followed
by Dr. Hata, who had been waiting for him, with his record
books. Ehrlich handed his hat and coat to Kadereit, who took
them and put them away in the study. Dr. Hata had already
placed the books on the bench under the windows and opened
them.

'Well, my dear Hata, what have you found out now?' asked
Ehrlich, coming near.

With repeated nods of his head, Dr. Hata replied:

'Always—606 best!'

'Incredible!' (unglaublich), said Ehrlich. 'What an incapable
good-for-nothing!' he exclaimed, his big eyes looking at Dr.
Hata over the tops of his spectacles. Hata looked scared and
stretched out his arms as if in defence. Ehrlich put his hand on
Hata's shoulder, soothingly, and shook his head.

'Oh, not *you*,' he said, '*not you*! No, the other fellow before
you,' he went on disgustedly. 'Not even in trypanosomiasis did
he find anything—der ungeschickte Taperkerl!' (the stupid
good-for-nothing!).

Then Dr. Hata beamed with delight and grinning broadly,
he repeated: 'Ungeschickte Taperkerl!'

'Wissen Sie, verstehen Sie,' said Ehrlich, 'that is the reason
why I told you at the very beginning that everything had to
be done again and again—and again! All had to be tested
minutely!' Then with a lively gesture he added: 'But I was
always convinced—have been convinced for years—that 606
must be good! Yet that fool found nothing—nothing!'

N

'Der ungeschickte Taperkerl,' repeated Hata nodding, enthusiastically.

Ehrlich, carried away by his excitement, took Hata by the arm and shook him ecstatically.

'And now—in spite of everything—it *really is* efficacious! And in syphilis too! Wissen Sie, verstehen Sie, dear Hata,' he went on, taking two thick envelopes with long reports from the piles of letters and unfolding one of them: 'See here, Professor Alt reports that he began by treating dogs to make sure that 606 was well tolerated. And then,' he tapped Hata's arm with his red pencil, 'and then two of his assistants injected themselves to find out the right doses and test the toleration of 606 by human patients.'

Hata laughed joyfully: 'Good, good—oh very good!'

'Yes, and then they gave a few paralysed patients injections of 606 and saw a slight improvement!'

Ehrlich unfolded the other thick report and went on speaking, jerking out his words:

'And then there is Professor Iversen at the St. Petersburg Hospital for Men. He has treated with 606 a great many patients with relapsing fever.'

He pointed with a sweeping gesture to the report:

'Completely cured! Yes, relapsing fever cured!'

Hata, overjoyed, his face bright and full of enthusiasm, clasped his hands and, pressing his elbows in to his body, moved his clasped hands up and down ecstatically as children do when they want to show their joy without making a noise about it. All he said was:

'Oh—good—very good!'

'But still, my dear Hata,' continued Ehrlich firmly, 'we must *repeat* the experiments again and again, to be *absolutely certain*!'

Hata replied, quite unmoved, with a deep bow: ' I—absolutely certain!'

.   .   .   .   .

Publications were prepared and appeared, and more valuable experience was gained. In the Summer of 1907 Ehrlich had sent some of the arsenical preparations which preceded 606, namely Arsacetin and Arsenophenylglycin, to Professor Albert Neisser of Breslau. Professor Neisser took them with him to Java, where he used them in experiments on monkeys and apes. When he returned to Breslau he continued the treatment of apes infected with syphilis, and in 1908 he published his results.[1] Some other publications followed about the necessity of carefully proceeding, step by step, in the treatment of human patients. Professor Julius Iversen of St. Petersburg published his reports concerning tolerability and the curative action in a great many cases of relapsing fever in Man, which he had treated at the Obuchow Hospital for Men.[2] And, in the section for skin diseases and syphilis at the hospital of Pavia in Italy, treatment with 606 was carried out with good and encouraging results by Professor Ascoli and Professor Pasini.[3] Professor Konrad Alt, after his first very conscientious and careful trials, now went on to use 606 in the treatment of his patients in the Landes-Heil- und Pflege-Anstalt at Uchtspringe (Altmark). So that he could take full responsibility for this, he had tested 606 for three months on dogs; and then, as has already been mentioned, two of his assistants studied its effect on human beings by injecting themselves.[4] As soon as Professor Alt had convinced himself that 606 was tolerated by Man without any harmful results, patients with paralysis in his hospital were treated with it, and further treatment of cases of primary syphilis was begun on a wide scale by Professor Schreiber at the Hospital of Magdeburg.[5]

Professor Iversen of St. Petersburg also continued to use it in clinical treatment. In January 1910, 606 was entrusted to two more large hospitals in Germany, and it was used extensively in cases of syphilis at the Hospital at Sarajevo. Professor Nägeli of Zürich reported that he had cured with 606 a leucaemia which up to then had always been fatal.

So at last Ehrlich no longer postponed publication, but decided to announce, together with Dr. Hata and Professor Schreiber, the facts about 606, and to make known to the whole medical world the results that had been obtained with this preparation.

[1] *Deutsche Medizinische Wochenschrift*, 1908, No. 35.
[2] *Münchener Medizinische Wochenschrift*, 1908, No. 35.
[3] Ehrlich–Hata: 'Die Chemotherapie der Spirillosen', Julius Springer, Berlin, 1910, p. 149.
[4] *Münchener Medizinische Wochenschrift*, 1910, No. 11.
[5] Ibid., 1910, No. 27.

CHAPTER XVII

INVENTION OF 606
ANNOUNCED TO THE WORLD

A GREAT number of medical practitioners and scientific men from all over Germany, as well as from foreign countries, were present at the Congress for Internal Medicine at Wiesbaden on 19 April, 1910.

Ehrlich spoke about the basis of experimental chemotherapy, and the preparation of chemical and especially arsenical compounds leading up to No. 606. He mentioned the exact animal experiments of Dr. Hata, the first treatment of human patients by Professor Iversen of St. Petersburg, who had cured relapsing fever with 606, the treatment of paralysis by Professor Alt, and the treatment of syphilitic patients by Dr. Schreiber of the Magdeburg Hospital.

Dr. Hata gave a detailed report of his curative experiments with syphilitic rabbits, at which he had worked for more than a year with frequent repetitions of extensive animal series.

Dr. Schreiber of Magdeburg gave an exact account of the first successful results in the treatment of syphilitic patients at his hospital with 606.

The Congress greeted these announcements with tremendously enthusiastic applause. All the daily papers reported this world-stirring invention with huge headlines, but most of them under the misleading name of 'Ehrlich-Hata 606', a name which was repeated for a long time, in spite of the fact that all the medical and other scientific periodicals gave a correct report of the events. From all that has been said here it is obvious that Dr. Hata had nothing to do with the invention itself. 606, like all the other substances previously prepared, was invented by Ehrlich *alone*. It must be repeated that 606 was worked out by Ehrlich, and patented, in 1907, while Dr. Hata did not come to Frankfurt until 1909. Dr. Hata himself never claimed any share of the credit for the invention of 606. Ehrlich was, however, too generous-minded to correct

the misunderstanding publicly, and besides, he had no time
to be troubled with such things.

Much credit was due to Dr. Hata for the way he had conscientiously carried out the animal experiments exactly as
Ehrlich told him, and, as he specially requested, with frequent
repetitions. It was also because of his untiring work that he
was able to prove the undoubted superiority of 606, whereas
his predecessor had obtained no result with it.

Some of Ehrlich's chemical assistants were pleased later on
to call themselves 'co-inventors' of 606. But they had merely
carried out Paul Ehrlich's instructions, sometimes even against
their will, as in the case of Atoxyl reported earlier. In the
preparation of 606 also they sometimes resisted Ehrlich's instructions, as will be shown.

After the Congress of Wiesbaden

Before the Congress at Wiesbaden, Ehrlich had firmly decided not to enlarge for some time the circle of clinics in which
606 was to be tested. But he had hardly returned from the
Congress before he was swamped with requests, made personally and by letter, from doctors who wanted to join this circle
and start treatment with 606 themselves.

After the Congress the days passed so quickly and so much
happened that it is difficult to record even the most important
events.

From early in the morning the long corridor of the Serum
Institute was full of visitors who had come straight from
Wiesbaden to see Ehrlich—visitors from all over the world.
There were also doctors from abroad in great numbers who
had not been at Wiesbaden but had come on account of the
newspaper reports and articles in all the scientific journals.
Patients also came, not knowing that Ehrlich had no clinic but
was wholly engaged in research work. They were, of course,
disappointed when they found he could not treat them; but
they were told to apply to one of the clinics where 606 was
being used.

Every medical visitor was kindly received by Ehrlich. He
spoke to them, asked for their addresses, gave them a few doses
of 606 for a trial or promised to send some as soon as possible.
The clinicians who received supplies of 606 had to promise,

however, to follow exactly Ehrlich's instructions as to its use. They also had to promise to select carefully the cases to be treated, and to take, for a start, only cases in the primary state of the disease; for at that time 606 could be supplied only in very small quantities, and the more advanced cases of the disease would naturally require longer and probably more intensive treatment. They had, furthermore, to promise to watch the treated patients with the utmost care, make a note in their records of the slightest change in the patients' general condition, and send Ehrlich a detailed report of everything that happened. Only in this manner, said Ehrlich, was it possible to come to a right judgment about the efficacy of 606, and only under these conditions could he promise to send more.

The first instruction which Ehrlich gave his own workers was that the chemical section of the Georg Speyer-Haus must interrupt all other chemical work and prepare nothing but 606 with the most careful observation of all the necessary precautions. A contract was made between the chemical factory in Höchst near Frankfurt and the Georg Speyer-Haus with regard to the manufacture of 606 on a large scale. This contract was not made with Ehrlich himself. He asked only a modest interest in it, which was laid down in an agreement between him and the Georg Speyer-Haus. With all possible speed, arrangements were made to produce 606 in the Speyer-Haus on as large a scale as the existing conditions and possibilities would allow. All hands there had to help, and, in addition, the Höchst chemical factory sent two of their most experienced chemists to give assistance.

A Name is Sought for 606

After repeated conferences, much thought and inquiries at the Patent Office, the name 'Salvarsan' was agreed upon and registration secured for it.

In the meantime there was much tongue-twisting over the monstrous chemical name of 606: dioxydiaminoarsenobenzene-dihydrochloride, the pronunciation of which can only be mastered by cutting it into its 'different chemical parts': dioxy-diamino-arseno-benzene-dihydrochloride. Even a poet could not resist producing an effusion about the 'gigantic name'.

At the beginning Ehrlich distributed 606 in such a way that he gave a small quantity to every doctor and every clinic without distinction, if he was asked for it and if he knew them by name or they were recommended to him. This method was in accordance with his sense of what was right and fair. Certainly the quantities of 606 which could be produced in the laboratories of the Georg Speyer-Haus were quite insufficient to meet the increasing demand. Even though all hands helped in preparing 606, the situation could not be much improved; for every day hundreds of letters came in asking for it. The gigantic installations at the Höchst Chemical Works, which were necessary for the manufacture of 606 on a large scale, had first to be devised and then built, a task which would take some months to accomplish.

Ehrlich did not really want too many clinics and doctors to undertake treatments with 606 at this stage. He wanted those who had already begun using it to pick out a small number of the most important cases only, so that these could be supplied with 606 without any interruption of the treatment, and accurate reports of the results would be possible. These methods, of course, limited the distribution, much to the annoyance of those doctors and clinics who were not able to have the preparation. This dilemma could not be avoided; for even when the Höchst Chemical Works finally began to supply a certain amount of 606, it was only possible to provide the clinics and doctors, by then increased to some hundreds at home and abroad, with what was absolutely necessary to prevent treatment coming to a standstill.

Many a professional expert of a dermatological University clinic made up his mind to ask Ehrlich for some 606 only after much hesitation. Because of this delay it often happened that another specialist practising in the same town who had come to Frankfurt and received some 606, even if only a little, immediately after the Congress, got ahead of him. This caused difficulties, jealousies and criticisms of Ehrlich. It was especially difficult when there really was no stock at all and he had to refuse 606 to these experts who were better qualified than the others to handle it and to undertake the necessary trials. Ehrlich never entrusted any specialist with 606 without knowing the type and extent of his practice, and receiving a solemn promise that he would not make a 'business' out of the treatment; but, having convinced himself of the ability and sincerity of the specialist, he gave him 606 with absolute confidence, if he had sufficient.

After a few months of trial treatment, when in spite of the most intensive work the production of 606 was by no means sufficient to cover the requirements of the hundreds of doctors and clinics who were using it, there came an extremely critical period. Ehrlich was obliged to ask everyone to 'limit the cases to be treated by very careful selection.' This was done by pasting small slips printed in red on to all letters.

So as to keep himself informed of the amount of Salvarsan sent away, Ehrlich began a peculiar control of his own. Every day the number of doses sent out and the names of the recipients had to be written on the inside of the door of one of the bookcases in his study! Ehrlich generally made these notes himself, and they had to contain the strength of the doses, the quantities and the date. He preferred his own calculations on the door of the bookcase to the regular books in which all the supplies sent out were recorded in the Georg Speyer-Haus. As about 65,000 doses were provided—of course without any charge—between June and December 1910, there had to be several columns reaching from top to bottom of the door. And during that time Ehrlich was often to be found sitting on his heels before the bookcase door making some additions. According to the number of doses a clinic or private practitioner had received, as shown in these notes, so Ehrlich from time to time wrote a letter asking for observations and information about results.

Every day a list was put up in the Speyer-Haus showing the stock of Salvarsan, giving separately the quantity available in the form of each of the conventional doses. The distribution was regulated by this list. Ehrlich decided what to send out, telling me the details, writing me a 'block' or leaving me the letters to deal with. If special doses were asked for, the demands often could not be fully met, but supplies were sent according to the doses and quantities in stock, as shown in the list. The parcels were made up and dispatched by the staff of the Speyer-Haus.

In order to get through all this tremendous amount of work it became necessary to answer some inquiries by a printed circular letter.

. . . . .

The sheer physical work which Ehrlich did during this trying period was enormous, apart from his scientific tasks. Day after day, for months and months after the Wiesbaden Congress, it was the same busy scene, increasing in activity all the time. Medical visitors from all parts of the world came to ask Ehrlich for Salvarsan, to tell him personally what observations they had made in the course of treatment, or to ask his advice about special cases. And there were also always patients who wanted to be treated by Ehrlich himself.

For everyone he had a kindly word. He gave some 606 to the doctors if he possibly could, or promised to send some later on. He listened to descriptions of uncommon cases, advised what to do, or what not to do. He listened also to the patients and their troubles, and gave them the address of a clinic or of a doctor for treatment according to the nature of their illness.

And all this was in addition to the urgent work at the laboratories, the work in the chemical section, the continued series of animal experiments; everything, day by day, requiring his presence and help. Ehrlich had to direct and watch over everything, for all efforts were being made to bring the preparation to perfection. The necessity which he found for keeping all his preparations protected from oxygen throughout the different stages of production has already been mentioned and also the dramatic scene which occurred between Ehrlich and some of his assistants over it. In the case of 606 these precautions were all the more necessary because the treatment of human patients was at stake. Later on Ehrlich himself said:

'Without this knowledge and the strictest observance of all necessary precautions it would have been impossible to introduce 606 into human medicine.'

As well as all this work every day, with its frequent excitements and occasional troubles, there were piles of written work to be done. The correspondence with the clinics and doctors using 606 was very heavy and often complicated. For Ehrlich did not want all the detailed reports he received for himself alone. He also informed the others of the results and observations, adding his own advice and practical suggestions, and asking what stage they had reached in the treatment of their patients. Details of this will be given later.

Many photographs and models showing syphilitic mani-

Ehrlich considering an animal experiment

festations before and after the treatment were sent in. Reports also came from tropical countries with photographs of cases of framboesia ('yaws') which had been cured with 606. This disease is called 'strawberry sickness' because of the appearance of the ulcers which look like strawberries and cover the entire body of the sick native. Every drawer and empty case gradually became filled with this valuable and instructive material. It could not be exhibited, for apart from the fact that there was too much to hang up on the walls, it was too dreadful to look at. In particular, the photographs of one case of a terribly malignant syphilis, found only in tropical countries, made the heart stand still to see it. It was horrible beyond description.

In addition, there was also something else of an entirely different nature which required Ehrlich's attention. From all over Germany people sent in crazy ideas for treatments and cures. Ehrlich was asked to examine and give his opinion on 'mixtures', 'cures', 'salves' and 'healing ointments'. He was asked to 'disclose the causal connection between the frequent cases of cancer and the increased use of tinned foods'; to examine 'extracts from plants which cure *all* diseases'; to work out a 'method of disinfecting human blood by the direct influence of light'; to study 'the effecting of cures by drinking petroleum in cases of cancer of the œsophagus' and the 'poisonous effect of potato flowers upon carcinoma', etc., etc. In spite of all his urgent work Ehrlich found time to answer such letters, replying politely, even to the most ridiculous, that he regretted not being able to work out the suggested ideas as his own problems and the work connected with them absorbed all his time.

People seeking positions asked Ehrlich to give them work. Many beggars implored his help. There were letters asking for autographs, and children who wrote that their birthdays were on the same day as his. People with the same name inquired if they were not relations. Patients who had been cured with 606 wrote to thank him. Patients who wanted to be treated— all were answered. To those who asked for an autograph he often wrote his chemotherapeutical motto: 'corpora non agunt nisi fixata'. To those who asked for help he sent a certain sum of money, without asking any questions. He was the kind of helper who didn't let his left hand know what the right hand was doing. He did not want to know all the circumstances, he did not want to be disappointed later, he simply wanted to help.

Ehrlich had a very sensitive mind, so much so that he was easily embarrassed by thanks or gratitude. Once, as though it was quite natural, he helped one of his collaborators out of a dilemma; and although he came in contact every day with the recipient of this great kindness he never mentioned the affair in any way and avoided anything that could possibly remind him of it. He was always ready to assist members of the medical profession or their families who were temporarily or seriously in want or distress. Here large sums were frequently involved, and it went without saying that they were regarded as presents, not loans. In this way he helped a well-known Frankfurt physician, supposed to be well off, who wrote simply:

'I cannot say anything except that my son is an officer in the Army.'

The money was asked for to cover his son's debts. Ehrlich had a very large sum transferred to him by his bank. Shortly after the outbreak of war in 1914 this son was killed, and Ehrlich asked me:

'What do you think? Shall I send a letter of condolence?'

I replied with a hesitant negative, and he said, as if a burden had been taken off him:

'No! You also think no!'

He helped and supported financially for months on end a physician whom he had known since the time when he was an assistant. Several times he sent considerable sums to the daughter of a well-known Frankfurt physician who was studying music against the wish of her parents, to help her out of temporary distress. For years he regularly assisted an able young investigator who never stayed in any of the positions which Ehrlich helped him to get, and because of his unreliability and lack of perseverance was always hard up. This affair finally turned out to be a constant annoyance to Ehrlich, who was at times literally bombarded with letters and telegrams from the man asking for money. At length Ehrlich's friends took charge of the matter, but they could not get rid of this troublesome young man until they threatened to take legal proceedings against him. Ehrlich himself would never have done that. He was against all violence and could not refuse when he was asked for anything.

Whenever a petitioner became too persistent, Ehrlich tried to restrain his own generosity—not by refusing the request altogether, but by sending a smaller sum than was asked for. At first, really angry that he should be importuned again so soon, Ehrlich would exclaim indignantly to me:

'But now, look here, I can't do it again so soon! Don't you agree with me?'

But after I had agreed with him and thought the matter was settled, he would return to the subject a little later and say:

'I think we really should at least send *something*!' And the letter he sent, almost apologising for not sending the full amount asked for, by no means discouraged the begging letter-writer from asking for more after another short interval. When people came in person to beg from him, Ehrlich very rarely refused their requests.

Why, one might think, did Ehrlich act in such a way, giving always more and more, and never taking steps to find out the real conditions under which these people lived? Well, if one knew his real nature which shrank sensitively from anything ugly or wrong, it was understandable. He could not say 'no', for his refusal might perhaps strike and hurt a person who was really in distress and deserved help. Ehrlich did not want to lose his idealism, his faith in honesty and what was good and kind. Yet he must sometimes instinctively have felt that something was wrong with the picture. Therefore he never asked about the why and the wherefore of the case if he was not spontaneously informed about them.

Ehrlich repeatedly received offers from destitute people to let him undertake medical experiments on them in return for a certain sum of money. He always refused decisively to do this, but never failed to give these wretched people who had lost all hope and faith in life some kindly comforting words and also material help.

This open-handed generosity not infrequently made Ehrlich hard up himself, so that he had no money left to pay his private bills. If, at such a time, Kadereit came with his petty-cash account for private telegrams and postage, mineral water, carriage fares, etc., and also showed the receipts for subscriptions to the numerous periodicals and scientific journals which Ehrlich ordered, a heavy expense in his small budget, Ehrlich generally threw up his arms in a gesture of mock despair, saying:

'Yes, but where do you think I can get all that money from? Do you imagine I can get it down from the sky?'

'That does no good, Herr Jeheimrat. It will have to be paid,' was Kadereit's dry unsympathetic answer.

'Oh yes, we must see what can be done,' replied Ehrlich resignedly. 'Remind me to-morrow.'

The next day Ehrlich would bring the money Kadereit needed to pay the bills. He had not forgotten, Kadereit did not need to remind him. Ehrlich had raised a loan from his wife. This was a rare event and caused a certain amount of controversy between them. It was the only point upon which Ehrlich and his wife were not in perfect harmony. On some special occasion Ehrlich wrote her a beautiful letter which Frau Ehrlich once showed me, thanking her affectionately for having always stood by him and for having kept the family so happily together. When he received the reprints of his publications he very often immediately sent one copy to his wife, with a dedication to his 'collaborator' as he sometimes called her. On the cover of one of these reprints—'Theorie der Lysinwirkung' (Theory of the action of lysins), published in 1899, he had written:

> 'Anbei folgt meine Neujahrsgabe
> die eben ich empfangen habe.
> So schnell sie aus dem Arm geschüttelt,
> so schnell sei Dir sie übermittelt.'

Literally translated this means:

> 'Herewith I send my New Year's gift
> Which I have only just received.
> As fast as from my hand it pours,
> I wish to think of it in yours.'

. . . . .

Ehrlich's deep sense of responsibility and his understanding sympathy with the sick and suffering are very clearly shown in his answers to their letters. The depths of despair revealed in the cries for help from these most miserable sufferers from a disease which ruined their lives were most pitiful. The annihilation of all domestic happiness, the self-condemnation and the cries of despair which were apparent in these letters shook the reader to the depths of his soul. Ehrlich's answers were full of the purest and most noble sympathy. He promised nothing, only pointing out the necessity of seeking medical advice and help; but he found soothing and comforting words for everybody. It was touching to see how the troubles of others made him suffer himself.

Professor Carl Ludwig Schleich of Berlin wrote of this great sympathy of Ehrlich's in his obituary, saying:[1]

'Whoever saw Ehrlich standing at a sick-bed, as I did, in the ward of a big children's hospital, must have been aware of the intense consciousness which this amazing man had of the immense problems which medicine had before it. I found it very touching to see how tenderly he stooped down to the little suffering patients, soothing and pleasing them with a cheerful word.'

[1] *Neue Rundschau*, Berlin, October 1915.

CHAPTER XVIII

SALVARSAN—EARLY TROUBLES

THE trying out of 606 in human medicine seemed to produce
many difficult problems. Anyone who knew Ehrlich's temperament will realise that the introduction of Salvarsan into general
medical practice meant a great responsibility and a heavy
burden on his soul. Whenever the appearance of undesirable
symptoms after treatment with 606 was reported by a clinic
or a private practitioner, Ehrlich was untiring in his efforts to
find out all the details about the treatment and would not rest
until the reason for the trouble had been found. He gave
orders ensuring that all possible precautions were taken during
the preparation of Salvarsan, so that any errors which might
occur during the manufacture, as well as during treatment,
could quickly be traced and all clinics and doctors informed.

Very often Ehrlich had a hard fight to induce certain clinics
and doctors to allow him to look into their methods of treatment; and sometimes extensive animal experiments were
necessary to find an explanation for the unexpected symptoms.

The following notes were written by Ehrlich himself about
the practical difficulties in trying out new preparations in
human pathology:[1]

'(1) Unlike experiments with animals, it is not possible
in the treatment of man to fix or use the "dosis maxima
bene tolerata" or maximal well-tolerated dose. It is therefore necessary to take great pains over carefully conducted
experiments, beginning with very small doses and gradually
increasing them in order to find out the most efficacious
dose.

'(2) In human beings primary sensitivities and acquired
hypersensitivities very often exist. More than half of all
the medical substances used produce undesired reactions

[1] 'Paul Ehrlich: Die Chemotherapie, ihre Grundlage und praktische Be-
deutung' (Chemotherapy, its basis and practical significance). *Handbuch der
Serumtherapie*, München, J. F. Lehmanns, Verlag, 1910.

even in small doses. With the new specific chemical preparations we must always be prepared for this possibility,
and realise that because of their powerful action grave
results may sometimes occur.

'(3) These primary sensitivities and acquired hypersensitivities are a very great hindrance. For this reason the
new treatment ought only to be tried out under conditions
where the most careful and continual attention to the
patient is possible.

'(4) Before treating a patient with the new preparations
it is well to find out whether in his case there has been
damage to any particular organ or part of the body so
that a "locus minoris resistentiae', or site of lowered resistance, is to be feared, which might be particularly threatened by the new preparation. If it is possible to test his
sensitivity by some harmless experiment, it is important
that this should be done. Before the new preparations
are released for use in general medical practice very
extensive tests must be made, and thorough experience of
indications, contra-indications, undesirable reactions, etc.,
must be obtained in order to avoid unfortunate results
which would bring this new field of investigation into
discredit.'

Great care and attention were always given to the detailed
reports of treatment with Salvarsan which came in every day
in large numbers. Ehrlich was deeply concerned over any
irregularity, even the slightest, and made every effort to discover the cause. When 606 was first used for treatment it was
given by intramuscular injection. But if this was done carelessly
or by an unskilled person into the muscle of the upper thigh,
the unfortunate result was often necrosis at the site of puncture.
When this happened the patient suffered great pain and could
not walk. It was called 'paralysis', and everyone was very
worried.

After a careful examination of all the circumstances in such
a case it became obvious that, in addition to the carelessness
of the doctor who gave the injection, a further mistake had been
made: the solution of 606 had been standing too long before
the injection was made, and oxidation through the access of

o

air had taken place, causing the colour of the solution to change from light yellow to dark brown.

As soon as this was discovered a new order, saying that the injections must be given immediately after the solution was made, had to be sent out to everyone concerned in the handling of 606.

In order to avoid oxidation during the various processes of manufacture of 606 in the Speyer-Haus, Ehrlich insisted that as well as carrying out the manipulations in a perfect vacuum, everything must be done to secure perfect work at all stages.

For this reason Ehrlich reminded Dr. Kahn, the head of the Chemical Section of the Speyer-Haus, that he had written him a 'block' on the subject.

'I have already received it, Herr Geheimrat,' replied Dr. Kahn, pointing to the note which lay on his table.

Nevertheless, Ehrlich stressed its importance again, saying:

'It is absolutely necessary and extremely important to take even more precautions than before in the preparation of 606. In the intervals between the different operations the products must not be kept merely in the refrigerator but actually packed directly into the ice. Only in this way can we be certain of avoiding oxidation throughout the different phases of manu-facture.'

But Dr. Kahn neither observed these strict orders himself nor told the other chemical assistants to do so. Perhaps, although they were absolutely necessary, he thought the instruc-tions superfluous. Perhaps he was so busy he forgot them. Certainly everyone was overworked and strained to the utmost during this period in both the Institutes; yet none more so then Ehrlich himself, and he was the most untiring. At all events, next morning Ehrlich came to see that his instructions had been carried out, and he found that nothing had been done. The products had been put in the refrigerator between operations, as always, but not packed into the ice as he had directed.

Angrily Ehrlich called Dr. Kahn to account, and a painful scene took place between them, similar to that described earlier between Ehrlich and Dr. Bertheim. Dr. Kahn could not refrain from contradicting his chief, saying that he was overworked and could not be everywhere at once. This was the reason why Dr. Kahn left the Speyer-Haus.

Ehrlich then entrusted Bertheim, who now completely acknowledged Ehrlich's authority in all chemical questions, with the temporary supervision of the Chemical Section. Since their earlier disagreement a confidential collaboration had developed between Ehrlich and Bertheim which continued undisturbed until the outbreak of the First World War. Then Bertheim was called up, and the very first day after he joined his unit he met with a sad accident which caused his sudden death.

.   .   .   .   .

In his endeavours to trace and eradicate undesirable reactions resulting from the injection of Salvarsan, Ehrlich went still further. He sent out a written inquiry to all concerned, referring to the necrosis seen in some cases and asking what kind of water had been used to make up the solution of Salvarsan; whether it was 'sterilised' or 'distilled'; and if the latter, where the distilled water had been obtained. He also asked what experiences the others had had in this respect.

Some answered that they always used sterilised water and never had any trouble. Others distilled it themselves. Some had even used ordinary plain water from the tap without any unfortunate results because they observed strictly all the other precautions. But the majority replied that they obtained distilled water from a pharmacist.

Of course, Ehrlich did not let the matter rest there. He ordered one of the chemists helping with the manufacture of 606 at the Speyer-Haus to send for distilled water from different pharmacies at Frankfurt. Kadereit brought in quite a number of small bottles containing distilled water, each bearing the label of the pharmacy where it had been bought. Together Ehrlich and the chemist examined the water under the microscope, and they both found that all the samples were heavily infected with air-borne bacteria.

The chemist remarked:

'It is really quite natural, Herr Geheimrat, when one realises that the big jars holding distilled water, which they have in all pharmacies, stand on a high shelf; and the water is drawn

out as required through a rubber tube. The receptacles stay
up there for a long time, and are only refilled when they are
empty.'

606
418

Injer trans technik

Fieber vielleicht durch
injection, die nicht
absolut steril bedingt!
Vielleicht denk man
geehaufte haut steri li
satecen!
Vielleicht sicherung durch
in teurine jod pin selen
Leopold anfragen!

606
418
Method of Infection
Fever perhaps caused by injection not being sterile! Perhaps the skin
was not properly sterilised! Perhaps this sterilisation could be ensured
by a thorough application of iodine. Ask Leopold! (Leopold Landau
of Berlin)

'Ja, natürlich, natürlich' (of course, of course), said Ehrlich.
'They are really like breeding cages for hatching bacteria!'

Then he added suddenly: 'We must send out new instructions for making the solutions.'

Ehrlich turned to Kadereit, who had been helping by handing him the bottles of water and was now just about to leave as the experiment was over.

'Tell Marquardt to come,' he said.

At that moment I was just entering the laboratory with the 606 distribution list, which I wanted to show Ehrlich for his approval, and a pile of letters for him to sign.

Ehrlich looked at the list and nodded consent. Then he said:

'We must write—new instructions.'

'Will you write straight away or sign the letters first, Herr Geheimrat?' I asked.

His only answer was to make a movement with his hand as though blotting something. He sat down at the little table on the left, on which was the primitive wooden inkstand and his enormous 30-cm.-long penholder, and began to sign his letters. He wrote very quickly, and then only a part of his name: 'P. Ehrl' with a long downward scrawl at the end. After a number of signatures this was reduced to 'Ehr', and finally only 'Eh', but always with a downward scrawl to finish. After each signature Ehrlich made a movement with his left hand as if to blot it. I held the blotter in my right hand, putting it down on each signature and then taking the signed letter away with my left hand—to finish as quickly as possible —until they were all attended to.

'Ah, that's that. Now we are going to write,' said Ehrlich. 'A-l-s-o: "Instructions for those who treat with Salvarsan: It has been found that the distilled water stocked by the pharmacists is in almost all cases heavily infected with air-borne bacteria. For this reason it is necessary to demand always *freshly distilled* water and to use *only* this for the solution of 606".'

When I looked up to ask to whom these instructions were to be sent, Ehrlich nodded, anticipating my question, and said:

'To be written to *everyone*.' Then he went on, walking up and down as was his custom: 'A-l-s-o: "Dear Dr. Bertheim, it is necessary to have new instructions for the solution of 606 printed and to include in them the attached directions . . ." '

This note to Dr. Bertheim was followed by more letters in quick succession:

'Dr. Spatz, *Münchener Medizinische Wochenschrift* (Munich Medical Weekly); Professor Dr. Schwalbe, Berlin, *Deutsche Medizinische Wochenschrift*: "Dear Colleague, please print the enclosed short notice—it is urgent!—in the next number of your journal: the frequent occurrence of necrosis after intramuscular injection of 606 has induced us to . . ." '

At this time Ehrlich also suggested to some of the people using 606 that, instead of giving intramuscular injections they should use the subcutaneous method: that is, injections just beneath the skin, not deep into the muscles. But even with this method infiltration round the site of injection would appear now and then, if the injection had not been made with the necessary care and skill. So Ehrlich still had to give incessant reminders of the need for the utmost attention to his instructions for clean and conscientious work.

On examination of one particular case of necrosis after injection with 606 in which the healing was very slow, it was found that there was dark-coloured matter lying wrapped up as in a capsule. Chemical investigation showed that this matter was an oxidation product of 606. The 606, after injection, had not been absorbed into the blood-stream, but remained at the spot and became oxidised. It could not have any effect on the disease, and on the contrary was even a hindrance to the healing of the necrosis. Evidently in this case a number of serious faults in the method of treatment had combined.

During all this period, for several months, the medical journals published innumerable articles about salvarsan treatment from all points of view. There were detailed descriptions of series of cases of human patients, with observations and results; reports of definite cures and complete recovery, some astonishing results; information about undesirable reactions, and Ehrlich's reasons for such incidents. Altogether the journals were largely filled with articles about 606, and the daily newspapers published endless articles about Ehrlich's personality and his wonderful invention.

CHAPTER XIX

KÖNIGSBERG CONGRESS AND LATER TROUBLES

FROM all parts of Germany, indeed from all over the world, they gathered together for the Congress at Königsberg in September 1910.[1] Clinicians, general practitioners, research workers in Natural Science, all were there. Many had used Salvarsan and wanted to report their work with it and the results they had obtained.

The Congress was a great success, and enthusiastic applause greeted Ehrlich when he appeared and spoke in the lecture theatre. This congress is even to-day often erroneously referred to as 'the historic occasion when Paul Ehrlich officially announced his invention of Salvarsan'. The "historic occasion" was really, as already shown, the Congress for Internal Medicine held at Wiesbaden on 19 April, 1910. During the five months between then and the Congress at Königsberg a great deal of work had been done in treatment with 606, and much experience had been gained and success achieved.

Nevertheless, Ehrlich did not cease to remind those at the Congress that they must not be content with a momentary success: that they must continue to observe strictly all necessary precautions in using Salvarsan; and that, by studying and watching the future conditions of every single case treated with Salvarsan, they could contribute to the development and improvement of the new therapy and so give a solid foundation to the building up of Chemotherapy as a whole. He ended his lecture with this appeal:

'The foundations are firmly laid in the ground. It is now our task to build the stately house upon them.'

It soon became evident how necessary were his words of warning and advice.

Two small events which occurred at the time of the Königs-

[1] Congress der Naturforscher und Aerzte (Congress of doctors of Natural Science and Physicians) at Königsberg, September 1910.

berg Congress show again Ehrlich's modesty and the simplicity of his character.

On the way to Königsberg he broke his journey at Stettin in order to visit Professor Ernst Neisser, a cousin of Professor Albert Neisser ('Albertus magnus') by then the well-known specialist in Dermatology at Breslau University and an old friend of Ehrlich's. Professor Ernst Neisser was the director of the City Hospital at Stettin. He was intensely interested in 606, taking a great part in trying it out in his hospital, and he had invited Ehrlich to come and see his treatments when passing through Stettin on his way to the Königsberg Congress.

Everything at the hospital had been arranged ready for this visit. The Director, Professor Ernst Neisser, the assistants, the nurses and the patients—all were in a state of great expectation. The doctors' usual morning round had, of course, been postponed until the arrival of the distinguished guest. All were eager to give him a hearty welcome.

But Ehrlich did not appear. They waited and waited. The patients began to get uneasy. The doctors and nurses were nervous; and the Director had to decide to begin the morning rounds. So they went, still hesitating, through one or two of the wards. They arrived at the third—and there they found Ehrlich in lively conversation with one of the male nurses. Evidently he had entered by a side-door and told the nurse his name: Dr. Ehrlich. The attendant had not understood the name, merely paying attention to the title 'doctor'. He had readily talked and given information to the unassuming visitor, and showed him everything which seemed to interest him. There was much surprise, laughter and hearty greeting when the Director, the assistants and the staff met him. The attendant was very confused, but Ehrlich laughed and was greatly pleased, and the whole assembly, including the patients, enjoyed the visit immensely.

Königsberg interested Ehrlich very much as a town, and immediately he arrived he visited the statue of Kant which made a deep impression on him. He often said it was the most beautiful monument he knew of.

On his way to the Congress hall he was detained somehow and arriving a fraction late he found all the doors were shut even though the Congress was only just due to begin. He tried several of the side doors, but none would open. Then he went back to the main entrance, and after trying in vain to open the door he began to knock. At last a great big door-keeper, tall and very dignified-looking, opened the door just a little and stared down disdainfully at the small man knocking so violently. Scornfully he said:

'What do you want . . . Sir? Everything here is full up!' and he tried to close the door again. But Ehrlich was pushing against it and crying out as loudly as he could:

'But I *must* get in! I *must*, I *must* get in!'

The big door-keeper bent forward a little and put out his hand to stop him.

'It is absolutely impossible! I have told you already, the hall is quite full!' he shouted down from above.

By this time the noise had attracted the attention of some of the visitors to the Congress who were walking impatiently up and down the entrance hall. They were waiting for Ehrlich, for naturally the Congress could not begin without him.

'What on earth is the matter?' they asked.

The door-keeper was raging because Ehrlich had succeeded in forcing the door open a little wider and squeezing himself into the gap, thus preventing the big man from closing the door again in his face. The door-keeper shouted back:

'It is this obstinate little fellow who is determined to get in!'

One of the members inside then recognised Ehrlich, squeezed in the doorway, and came running to help him, pushing the big attendant aside.

'But that is a very great man!' he cried out. 'That is Ehrlich himself!'

Then, of course, Ehrlich was at once pulled into the hall and enthusiastically cheered by all assembled there. The door-keeper looked very silly, and fled to the background in confusion.

I recently made the acquaintance in Paris of the former representative of one of the great chemical firms in Berlin who had known Ehrlich at this time. Speaking about the Salvarsan period and the two important congresses in 1910, at which he had also been present, he said with enthusiasm that never again had he seen anything like the Königsberg Congress.

. . . . . .

More Exciting Events. The Intravenous Injection

When he returned from Königsberg there was a pile of letters and reports waiting for Ehrlich to attend to, and he was again extremely busy. He first read all the letters at home and then, at the Institute, he took some out of the pile and read them again. He was smoking a cigar in an excitable way, and kept walking up and down the laboratory with an angry frowning expression on his face. I showed him the list for the despatch of Salvarsan. He looked at it and handed it back without a word. Then after a short pause he said, his voice sounding strangely depressed:

'A-l-s-o . . . let us write.'

At that moment Professor Sachs came in.

'Good morning, Herr Geheimrat,' he said.

'Tag ook, my dear Sachs,' replied Ehrlich.

Taking advantage of this interruption, I ran out to give Kadereit the list for the despatch of Salvarsan, which he immediately took over to the Speyer-Haus. As I returned to Ehrlich's room I heard Professor Sachs say:

'Königsberg has been a great success has it not?'

'Yes . . . yes . . . it was very nice there. . . .' said Ehrlich. Then, very agitatedly, as though something explosive inside him had been touched off by Dr. Sachs's entrance, he burst out:

'You cannot have any idea, my dear colleague, what sort of blockheads one has to deal with!' He pounded the letters with the palm of his hand. 'Those wretched scoundrels are really going to ruin Salvarsan entirely, because they will not pay attention to any of my instructions!'

Dr. Sachs looked scared and asked:

'What is the matter now, Herr Geheimrat?'

He took the letters which Ehrlich handed him and read them through, shaking his head. Evidently they were reports of further trouble when using Salvarsan.

'It is almost unbelievable,' he said. 'Always this carelessness with the water, lack of skill in giving the injections, puncture of the muscle, necrosis. . . .' He looked at Ehrlich, shaking his head disapprovingly. 'It is nothing but incompetence which should have been overcome long ago. And the unfortunate patient must pay for it!'

'The patient *and* Salvarsan,' replied Ehrlich angrily. Clench-
ing his fists he went on: 'But I shall show them, I shall force
my will on them! I shall introduce intravenous injection and
insist on it for all treatment with 606, to put an end to this
hoggish, dirty behaviour once and for all.'

'They will all object to that rule,' remarked Dr. Sachs
critically, 'because they are not accustomed to intravenous
injection—it is only used in cases of extreme emergency.'

'Then they must learn how to make intravenous injections. I
shall demand it and compel them to do it,' cried Ehrlich
loudly, trembling with excitement.

Dr. Sachs was still doubtful.

'They will miss the vein and make the injection beside it, or
they will go right through the side of the vein, and either way
there will be inflammation.'

'At first, perhaps, yes; but they will soon get used to it—if
they have to. And then this sort of thing cannot happen.'
Ehrlich banged his fist again indignantly on the letters which
he had taken back from Dr. Sachs. 'Then the blood will get
the better of the dirt.'

Dr. Sachs nodded in agreement. Then, having grown calm
again, Ehrlich recommenced the interrupted dictation.

'A-l-s-o, was hatten wir gesagt?' (what did we say?)

' "Dear Benda, . . . I suppose that a certain receptor for the
radicle of acetic acid must exist in the cells, and that it must
be just this aceticoceptor which is responsible for the efficiency
of Arsenophenylglycin." '

Then he suddenly thought of something quite different he
wanted to do in the Speyer-Haus.

'Ach, . . . er—lauben Sie mal . . .' (Oh, excuse me . . .), he
said, breaking off and going out. His thoughts had again carried
him away into the world of his own.

When he was like this it was no use waiting for Ehrlich to
return from the Speyer-Haus, so I usually went upstairs to my
own room to work. Sometimes, however, he came back almost
at once, and then he called out my name from the entrance,
shouting: 'Markart!'

Coming down quickly I would call out to Kadereit that I
had heard so as to save him coming to fetch me.

. . . . . .

Professor Heubner of Göttingen published in 1911 a collection of scientific articles about Salvarsan, with a preface by Ehrlich. Writing about the methods of trying out 606 in human medicine,[1] Professor Heubner said:

'Another of Ehrlich's great merits is the classical example he has given of the ways and means by which Salvarsan has been tested. If we compare this publication with Ehrlich's lecture at the Wiesbaden Congress only seven and a half months ago, it is plain that the result arrived at in that time is a triumph of organisation—one might say as great a moral achievement as the discovery of the effective chemical structure is a scientific one.'

Grave Incidents and their Explanation.

After this trying and difficult period, Ehrlich at last consented to take a little rest. Late in the autumn of 1910 he went to Baden-Baden for a few weeks' holiday accompanied by his wife. I followed some days later, with the mail that had arrived in the meantime, to take down Ehrlich's dictation in answer to it.

Ehrlich sat at a small table in the lounge of the Hotel Regina, reading the letters I had brought with me.

'There is also a telegram from Vienna which arrived just as I was leaving the Institute to come here, Herr Geheimrat,' I said, handing it to him.

He opened and read it, and a terrified expression appeared on his face. Frau Ehrlich had just joined us, and was greeting me when she suddenly looked at her husband in alarm and exclaimed:

'Paul, for Heaven's sake, what is the matter?'

I whispered to her: 'A telegram from Vienna.'

Ehrlich lifted both his clenched fists up to his head with a stifled groan.

'This is unbelievable—it's terrible!'

Frau Ehrlich picked up the telegram and read it.

'Good heavens! Lost hearing—after Salvarsan injection—deafened! What have they been doing?'

Still trembling with excitement, but already a little calmer, Ehrlich said:

[1] 'Therapeutische Monatshefte', 1911, Bd. 25, page 318.

'Yes, what *have* they been doing? It's certain something has gone very wrong!'

I, too, was stupefied, not knowing before what the telegram contained. Then Ehrlich suddenly became quite calm and began giving directions, saying to me:

'Please, we must send telegrams. To Professor Finger, Vienna: "Request immediate telegraphic reply what doses were injected. How was the injection made." And to Dr. Bertheim: "Please find out immediately from which batch Professor Finger received Salvarsan . . . who else has received from the same batch . . . and report to me immediately." '

I hurried out to send off the telegrams. By the time I returned, Ehrlich had already worked out the entire plan of action. He said to his wife:

'I must go back to Frankfurt. I cannot do anything else.'

'Then we shall pack at once and go back to-morrow,' she replied. Ehrlich nodded gravely and she went upstairs. Then he turned to me:

'Please go back this afternoon, we shall come to-morrow, and give Sachs the following note: "Dear Sachs, we must immediately ask the Institute of Pathology to make exact studies of the anatomical conditions in the acoustic canal and the adjoining parts of the brain—very urgent".'

I packed up all the letters and papers, including the ominous telegram, and bade Ehrlich good-bye.

'I am terribly sorry, Herr Geheimrat, that you have such alarming news again.'

He grasped my hand and nodded sadly.

'Until to-morrow,' he said.

He remained at the empty table, his head resting on his hands, his face overshadowed with sorrow.

.   .   .   .   .   .

When Ehrlich arrived back at Frankfurt the telegraphic reply from Vienna had already come and Dr. Bertheim had obtained the necessary information. Ehrlich said to Dr. Sachs:

'Now you see, in spite of all my warnings against injecting small doses, Professor Finger has given the patient an injection of 0·1 g. . . . you understand me, 0·1 g., the very smallest dose possible! And what he tells of the patient having lost his hearing, being deaf, is nothing but a relapse of the disease after insufficient treatment.'

Dr. Sachs nodded. 'You will also receive the result of the anatomical studies at the Pathological Institute to-day,' he said.

'Good, thank you, my dear Sachs.' Then turning to me Ehrlich asked:

'Have the telegrams to the other clinics been sent off?'

'Yes, Herr Geheimrat, the answers should come very soon.'

'Good.'

Then an assistant from the Institute of Pathology at the University of Frankfurt came in, bringing with him a prepared skull for demonstration. Ehrlich greeted him:

'Tag ook, lieber Kollege. (Good day, dear Colleague.) What did you find?'

'I have brought the prepared skull with me, because it shows quite clearly the narrow anatomical conditions in the acoustic canal and the connection with the respective parts of the brain,' he replied.

The skull was examined minutely, the Assistant demonstrating with a pair of forceps the different parts. Ehrlich nodded and then, after a period of deep meditation, walking up and down, he said:

'It is now quite clear to me. The small dose of Salvarsan, 0·1 g., acted as a stimulating rather than a curative dose. The spirochaetes lying in the acoustic centre were only partly destroyed. Those that resisted treatment and remained at the spot found all the more space and opportunity for growing and multiplying. In consequence, the ability to hear of course suffered, and the patient became deaf. But this will certainly be cured by continuation of the treatment with doses which are not too small. This case is nothing but a neural relapse.'

Soon Kadereit came bringing a number of telegrams which had just arrived. Ehrlich opened them, and his worried expression brightened. He handed the telegrams one after the other to Dr. Sachs, who, after reading them, gave them to the Assistant from the Pathological Institute. Taking a deep breath, Ehrlich said:

'The answers—all on the same lines: good curative results; no disturbance whatever. . . .'

Two more telegrams were brought in by Kadereit.

'The postman had forgotten them,' he said.

Ehrlich opened them and read, then said:

'Exactly like the others. We must write immediately a paper explaining this case.' He turned to me:

'Now, let us write: "With reference to the case of 'deafness' after injection with 606 in the Clinic of Professor Finger of Vienna: the 'neural recurrences' are nothing but the expression of an incomplete sterilisation. The appearance of neural recurrences is avoided by a really intensive initial treatment. When lesions are very scarce, particularly those which are located in nerves, and are very difficult to approach, some of the germs may remain untouched and give rise to recurrences." That is to be sent off immediately, for early publication, to the editors of the medical periodicals,' he instructed.

Ehrlich asked Professor Finger to give this patient of his larger doses of Salvarsan. In a short time the 'deafness' had completely disappeared.

. . . .

In December 1910 the Chemical Works completed the installations necessary for the manufacture of 606, tried it out, and produced considerable quantities, sufficient to cover the first requirements of all the pharmacies. Now Salvarsan could be bought readily, and supplies from the Speyer-Haus were no longer necessary. As has already been mentioned, since the announcement of the invention of 606 was made at the Wiesbaden Congress in April 1910, more than 65,000 doses had been sent out, free of charge. The private record of what was sent out, which Ehrlich kept in pencil on his cupboard door, had reached the bottom of the inside of the door. Now he could close it.

. . . .

The writer of Ehrlich's obituary notice in *The Times* said in August 1915:

'Neither lack of food or sleep was ever allowed to interfere with the study of a problem.'

Life did not become quieter or more peaceful for Ehrlich. He still had to go on giving advice as before, helping with any problems and correcting anything which went wrong. There was the same amount of correspondence every day. In fact, it was increased by long reports about cases which, at Ehrlich's request, had to be watched for a considerable time.

When relapses were reported Ehrlich asked for every detail of the treatment, especially what doses had been given at the start. These investigations always showed that the relapses occurred when, through undue caution, only *small* doses had been injected. Ehrlich had to keep on emphasising this fact:

'Treatment should not be frittered away with too small doses, especially as the small doses encourage the development of relapses.'

In cases where large doses had been given, relapses did not take place. And whenever relapses appeared after the injection of small doses they disappeared when treatment was continued with doses sufficiently large.

Ehrlich's own health suffered very much from the perpetual striving and watching to see that his instructions were properly carried out. The introduction of intravenous injection into general use required much advocacy and hard work, though it was finally accomplished. Ehrlich gave himself no rest; he would not even take a few weeks' holiday, lest some stupid mistake should occur in his absence if he ventured to turn his back and temporarily withdraw his guiding hand.

.   .   .   .   .

One day Ehrlich had just finished a long dictation and I was about to leave the room, when Kadereit entered to announce Dr. Arthur von Weinberg, who had been a friend of Ehrlich's for some years. The visitor followed close behind Kadereit, so that I was caught in the corner by the door and could not get out of the room.

Dr. von Weinberg, Director of the Cassella Chemical Works at Mainkur near Frankfurt, had supported Ehrlich's chemical and chemotherapeutical investigations long before the Speyer-Haus was built. He had allowed one of his chemical experts, Dr. Ludwig Benda, who has already been mentioned in this story, to work almost exclusively for Ehrlich and according to his instructions.

Giving his guest a hearty welcome, Ehrlich said:

'Tag ook, my dear friend, nice of you to come! When Mahomet does not come to the mountain—wissen Sie—verstehen Sie!'

They were both laughing, and Dr. von Weinberg replied:
'Yes indeed, that is so!'

They were standing near the door, and still I could not get out. Pointing towards me, Ehrlich remarked cheerfully:
'You know my right and my left hand, dear friend?'

Dr. von Weinberg nodded kindly, greeting me.

'Do you know what she has done?' went on Ehrlich.

'No,' said Dr. von Weinberg amiably, 'what mischief has she been up to?'

With an air of importance Ehrlich answered, smiling:

'She has been working all this time almost day and night, and has never had more than four hours' sleep—four hours!' Then smiling at me, he added: 'But now she must have a few weeks' holiday.'

'Certainly she deserves it,' laughed Herr von Weinberg. 'And what about you?' he continued, putting his hand on Ehrlich's shoulder. 'You need a rest even more—much more!'

Ehrlich shrugged his shoulders.

'Oh, my dear friend,' he said, 'I cannot think of going away. Those incapable good-for-nothings (Diese ungeschickten Taperkerle) would spoil the entire system of Salvarsan therapy if I did not keep an eye on every detail.' His features became grave. 'You cannot imagine,' he went on, 'how difficult it is to get my instructions carried out and to force them to do the right things!'

Von Weinberg nodded sympathetically.

'But you will succeed in the end, dear friend. With your determination and authority you will get your way. You have already proved it with the intravenous injection—I would never have believed that to be possible. It is of the greatest importance for all treatments which are required to act quickly. Just think what it means to medicine as a whole—one cannot picture what it may lead to!'

By this time Ehrlich was cheerful again and said happily:

'Yes, yes, of course, of course! It was damned hard work, I can tell you,' he went on emphatically. 'But it was necessary!'

Taking a deep breath, Ehrlich then switched over to the new ideas which filled his mind. 'By the way, did you read my paper—wissen Sie—verstehen Sie—the paper in honour of Waldeyer?'

P

Dr. von Weinberg nodded.

'Yes, excellent, very fine!'

After offering his guest a cigar, Ehrlich went on quoting parts of the publication:[1]

'*Eo ipso*, I have come to the conclusion that the curative organic substances are captured and fixed, not by a single chemoceptor only, but by a number of them which come into action simultaneously, in the same way as the pins with which the collector fixes down the different parts of a specimen butterfly, wissen Sie, verstehen Sie! And so, *re vera*, Arseno-phenylglycin is primarily anchored into the protoplasm by the acetoceptor and simultaneously by the arsenoceptor. In the case of Salvarsan it is the arsenoceptor and an orthoamino-phenoloceptor which come into action equally. Thus, keeping the arsenobenzene as an example, *re vera*, the Side-chains added to the benzene-ring act as organs, with which the arsenic-radicle can be forced to take effect upon the different parasites, according to the kind of chemoceptors which are preformed in these parasites.'

While thus speaking, Ehrlich had been walking up and down as usual, sketching diagrams on the bookcase and doors in passing, and now and then dabbing at Dr. von Weinberg's coat sleeve with the point of his coloured pencil or his cigar. Full of admiration his friend remarked:

'Another of your fundamental conceptions!'

Ehrlich was never content to rest on his laurels. As Felix Pinkus said in his obituary notice:

'In spite of all the new and enlightening progress which Paul Ehrlich's work revealed, he always had the feeling that he had only just begun. What the world considered to be the final result of Ehrlich's intensive research was to Ehrlich himself only the beginning of still greater explorations into the unknown. He never enjoyed a success in tranquillity and peace, but soon left behind the result just attained, and rushed forward in a profusion of deductions which carried him on with equal rapidity to a still higher peak of perfection; then this point, once reached, was in its turn again surpassed.'

[1] Literal translation from Ehrlich's 'Festschrift' in honour of Professor Waldeyer, his teacher at the Strassburg University.

CHAPTER XX

EHRLICH AND HIS GRANDCHILDREN

EHRLICH continued energetically to resist all suggestions that he should take a holiday, insisting on staying at Frankfurt to see what was going on. As he would not go away, his grandchildren came there to visit him. They were Hans Schwerin, aged nine, and his brother Günther, aged six, children of Ehrlich's elder daughter Steffa, who had married Dr. Schwerin of Breslau; also Susi Landau, aged seven, her sister Dolli, aged five, and their little brother Mathias, who was three. These were the children of Marianne, Ehrlich's second daughter, who had married Dr. Landau, Professor of Mathematics at Göttingen University.

Having all these children in the house made things very lively, and Ehrlich enjoyed it immensely. Hans Schwerin and Susi Landau had visited their grandparents before, and so were better acquainted with the habits of Grandpa Ehrlich than the younger children were. It was therefore only natural that they should lead the others.

Early one Sunday morning the children tiptoed downstairs from their attic bedrooms at the top of the house, Hans and Susi first, the others following them. They stood outside the door of Ehrlich's bedroom, listening silently. They heard Grandpa singing 'On the green banks of the Spree' to himself, and they chuckled, for he sang out of tune—he always did. Then Hans plucked up his courage, knocked very gently at the door and, opening it just a little whispered through the crack:

'Hullo, Grandpa!'

From inside the room Ehrlich replied:

'Good morning, little Hans.'

At this, Hans and Susi squeezed themselves through the partly open door. Trying hard to seem grown-up, Hans said with an air of great importance:

'The children are waiting to see you, Grandpa.'

While Susi said, giggling:

'Oh Grandpa, you are still in the dark!'

'Yes, my dear,' he replied. 'In the dark you can whisper well.' (This is a much-used expression in German, for the sake of the rhyme: 'Im Dunkeln ist gut munkeln'.) 'Come in, all of you, but don't make a noise.'

They tiptoed into the room, and soon there were sounds of the splashing of water and the merry laughter of the children in which Ehrlich joined; though now and again he checked this noise with a warning:

'Ssh . . . ssh . . . softly . . . softly.'

Finally they all trooped out again, Hans in the lead, carrying a bottle of poisonous-looking green liquid carefully in front of him. The others followed silently on tiptoe.

Ehrlich's wife was just coming out of her room in her morning gown, and on seeing the children she exclaimed, laughing:

'Now children, what mischief have you been up to? You must have been disturbing Grandpa terribly. And whatever have you got there, Hans?'

She took the bottle and looked at it, shaking her head. Hans explained very solemnly, saying:

'I have been doing some chemical work with Grandpa already. We have made a wonderful hair tonic.'

His grandmother handed back the bottle and said, smiling:

'Really? But it does not look very tempting, Hans, with that poisonous green colour!'

'Oh but it is, Oma,' said Hans vehemently. 'And it really works marvellously—you must try it, Oma. . . .'

He tried to give her back the bottle, but she stopped him, saying laughingly:

'No, no, Hans, you must keep that all to yourself!'

The other children had been silently looking on, and now Dolli spoke up, holding her little brother by the hand.

'Oma dear,' she said, 'we should, oh we should *so much* like to see the green frog!'

The others clasped their hands in glee, calling out excitedly:

'Oh yes, Oma, the green frog, please!'

'Very well then, come with me,' said Frau Ehrlich.

They all went into Ehrlich's study, where the tall bell-jar

containing the frog was standing on one of the window-sills,
But the frog was hiding under the green plants at the foot of
the glass, and the little ladder which he used to climb up was
unoccupied. The children were disappointed.

'But he must just once more come out of his little green
garden and climb up the ladder!' they said.

'He will only do that when nice weather is coming,' explained their grandmother, 'and I do not think it will be nice
weather to-day.'

'Oh, Oma!' exclaimed the children sadly.

At this moment, Ehrlich came in smoking his cigar, but he
put it aside when he saw the children. Through the half-open
door the thick cigar-smoke which filled his bedroom could be
seen. He was carrying his cigar-box and a pile of the inevitable
'blocks', which he put down on the table, and came over to
the window where the children were.

Kadereit had just come into the study by the other door
from the hall, carrying his big portfolio full of letters. He was
greeted with a great shout from the children, in which Ehrlich
also joined:

'Kadereit, Kadereit, the flies, the flies!'

With a little smile Kadereit hurried to please the children,
and while they watched excitedly he took out the piles of
letters from his case and then produced a large-sized test tube
carefully stopped up with cotton wool. The test tube was full
of flies.

'You know, children,' said Ehrlich with a smile and a side-
ways glance at Kadereit, 'you know Kadereit raises all the
flies in the stables of the Institute. He has made a special study
of breeding them, and then when they have grown big enough
he catches them with a butterfly net.'

At this the children protested, saying:

'Oh, but Opa, that is not possible! They would all get out
thought the holes in the net!'

Kadereit was getting ready to hand the test tube to Ehrlich,
and they watched every movement, fascinated. Ehrlich replied
mysteriously:

'Oh, no! You see, children, Kadereit has a special trick to
keep them in the net.' He looked hard at the children over the
tops of his spectacles: 'Once the flies are caught in the net they

can never get out. They are kept there by a magic spell—by
witchcraft!'

'By witchcraft, Opa?' repeated the children, holding their
breath in amazement. 'But how does he do that?'

Ehrlich nodded solemnly in confirmation, and Frau Ehrlich
laughed. Kadereit handed the tube to Ehrlich, passing it over
the children's heads while they tried excitedly to clutch it, and
said drily, without moving a muscle of his face:

'Yes, that is not at all easy. But to-day there were plenty
of flies—I think it is going to rain.'

By this time Ehrlich had begun to feed the frog with the
flies, and the children watched with absorbed attention. They
were very excited and shouted for joy when the frog jumped
about and snapped at the flies to catch them. The frog climbed
a little way up the ladder to catch the flies more easily, and
Ehrlich promptly explained that this meant a change for the
better in the weather.

'You see, children,' he said, 'Kadereit has only to come in
and the weather improves and the sun starts to shine. Kadereit
brings all that with him.'

But the children exclaimed, sceptically:

'Oh Opa, how could he do that? How could he bring the
nice weather with him?'

Ehrlich hugged them affectionately and said:

'How did *you* bring the nice weather with you? Just your
being here means sunshine to me! But now you must go out
for a walk and leave me. Opa has work to do.'

'But must you really go to the Institute to-day, on Sunday?'
asked Frau Ehrlich.

'Oh yes,' he replied, 'on Sundays I can always work best—
is not that so, Kadereit? Nobody annoys or interrupts me.'

Kadereit's expression was not exactly enthusiastic, but he
nodded, nevertheless.

'Oh well, if you must, you must,' said Frau Ehrlich. 'Come
along, children,' she said, stretching out her hand.

.   .   .   .   .

In the afternoon they met again on the small terrace outside
the dining-room. All the houses in the block had small gardens
behind them which joined together. The dividing walls were
hidden by trees and shrubs, even the other houses were almost

hidden so that the gardens looked like a small park. There was a little grass plot in the centre of Ehrlich's garden, with a flower border to the left and free-flowering rose bushes all round the lawn. There were shrubs and trees, a few birches, poplars and mountain ashes, against the rear wall.

A door led from the dining-room on to the terrace, and a few steps went down at one side from the terrace into the little garden. A big table was set out for tea, and there Ehrlich joined his wife and grandchildren. As always, he had with him his cigar-box and his writing materials. Dora, the maid, brought the tea, with chocolate for the children to drink, and they all enjoyed being out-of-doors on this lovely Sunday afternoon.

'Have you been working very hard, Grandpa?' asked Hans.

'Yes, of course, little Hans, of course,' said Ehrlich. 'I must *always* work hard.'

When tea was finished he said to the children:

'Come, let us go and look at our little tree.'

The children jumped up quickly and ran down the stone steps. The little seedling by the wall had already grown to be a little ash tree.

'Look, children, it has grown quite a bit more!'

They gathered around Ehrlich, exclaiming: 'Oh yes, yes!' And he, stretching out his arms, said:

'Oh, isn't that lovely? But we must not forget to feed the birds,' he went on. 'Come. Do you hear them? They are all waiting, ready for their food.'

Dora had meanwhile cleared the table, leaving his cigars and writing things handy and also a bowl full of crumbs. At the end of the terrace and beyond, a noisy lot of birds were waiting. Ehrlich sat down at the table and spread out the crumbs for the birds, saying to the children:

'Do not come too near, my dears, in case you scare the birds away.'

The birds came hopping on the table, picking up the crumbs, to the great delight of the children, who were kept by Frau Ehrlich and Dora near the dining-room door.

'Just look at the little blue-tit,' he called to them. 'It always comes back, again and again.'

The children craned their necks to see and cried out:

'Oh yes, yes!'

'Now we shall see whether Mr. Bullfinch prefers large or small crumbs,' said Ehrlich, putting a few larger pieces among the crumbs on the table. But it was not the bullfinch who took them, but two small coal-tits, who hurled themselves upon the big pieces and tried with all their strength to drag them away. Ehrlich laughed heartily.

'There, just look at the cheeky little creatures,' he said. The children shouted with merriment, clapping their hands, and then, of course, the whole assembly of birds flew up and away.

'And now Grandpa must work, children,' said Ehrlich, nodding kindly to them all, and to his wife.

'Good night, children,' he said.

'Good night, Opa,' they chorused. And as soon as they had gone he went on working and smoking.

.   .   .   .   .

Ehrlich loved to tell fairy tales to the children. They were mostly ones which he invented himself, and metamorphosis and witchcraft played a part in them, evidence of his chemical attitude to life, even to fairy tales.

Hans Schwerin once told me the following story about his grandfather: One evening when the children were staying with their grandparents, Ehrlich went up into the nursery while they were having their supper.

'Well, children,' he said, 'what's that nice thing you have got there?'

'Rice pudding, Opa,' they replied.

Grandpa Ehrlich stretched up his head and sniffed and said: 'Oh, how good!' He then recited this little poem about rice pudding, much to the children's delight:

'Die Speise	'Pudding of rice,
vom Reise	All wise men praise it,
die lobt jeder Weise,	All old men praise it,
die loben die Greise	They sit in a circle
sie sitzen im Kreise.'	And find it nice.'

The children were thrilled. 'Opa, you can make poems too!' they said.

'Of course I can make poems, and I know fairy tales as well. And they are all things that happened to me myself!'

The children jumped up, clustering around him.

'Oh, Grandpa, tell us, please, please. . . .'

'All right, let us all sit down here,' he said, taking a seat on the sofa. The children brought their little chairs and sat down close beside him. Then Ehrlich began:

'Well, this morning when I had gone deep into the woods . . .'

'But, Opa,' cried Günther, 'this morning you were at the Institute!'

'Yes of course I was, but *before that* I had been deep into the woods. And there I met a magician. And this magician had worked a magic spell against a big tree, so that the tree was no longer a tree, but had changed into . . . into a donkey! But there was something very funny about this donkey, because it had crept out of a pearl. And the pearl was not really a pearl at all, but a bewitched princess, the daughter of a king. . . .'

The children listened breathlessly, and when the story was finished, Susi asked:

'Opa, did you see the magician really and truly?'

'Yes, really and truly. Just think of it, he had green hair!'

By now Dora had come in and was waiting to put the children to bed.

'Do you not believe it, children?' said Ehrlich. 'Well, that magician was kind enough to let me have his head. . . . Dora, please fetch the magician. . . .'

The children shivered a little with fear and excitement, and Dora went out of the room returning with Ehrlich's big leather portfolio, which she handed to him, trying hard to keep a serious face. Ehrlich opened the case and took out of it with great care an object which was wrapped up in white tissue paper. The children were wide-eyed with expectation. Ehrlich unpacked the mysterious object and then burst out laughing as he put it on the table. There it stood, a head modelled in a reddish-coloured clay. On top of it grass seed had been sown in a thin layer of soil, and it had sprung up green and soft just as hair would grow on the head. All the children gathered round to stroke this 'hair' with great delight and merriment. Dora also laughed, but at length she reminded them:

'Now you must go to bed, children.'

'Well, I must say good-night,' said Ehrlich. Then, as he turned to leave the room, he added: 'You know, children, when I went to Berlin the other day I brought back ever so many nice things for you. But I forgot them, and left them in the train!'

'What sort of things had you brought with you, Opa?' inquired the children.

'There was a globe, a whole globe of the earth it was, with people and railways, yes, and real live animals. . . . But I expect the ticket-collector who found it will have lots of fun with *his* children playing with it.'

'Oh, Opa,' the children cried out regretfully, 'a whole globe of the earth—what a pity!'

Ehrlich had reached the door. 'Sleep well, children,' he said. 'When I go on a journey again I shall not forget your presents, you may be sure.'

'Good night, dear Opa,' said the children sleepily.

'Good night!'

CHAPTER XXI

MORE DISCOVERIES IN SYPHILIS

WHEN I returned from my holiday I found Ehrlich in his laboratory making test tube experiments as usual and searching for something among his collection of chemicals.

'Good morning, Herr Geheimrat,' I said.

Ehrlich left his experiment and came to meet me with a kind smile on his face. Shaking hands with me, he said:

'Nice to have you back again.'

This welcome made me very happy, for I took it to mean that he had no fault to find with my work, and I could not have wished for higher praise.

As soon as he returned to his experiment, Ehrlich began to dictate:

'A-l-s-o,' he said, 'Jetzt wollen wir schreiben' (Now let us write): ' "My dear friend Gabriel, I really shall now follow your advice and shut off steam for a while and take better care of the engine. Actually, it has not been the work itself which has exhausted me, but the excitement, disturbances and disagreeable incidents connected with it which upset my nerves. When I come to Berlin again I will tell you all about the difficulties I have had. Laboratory work is child's play in comparison: either a thing will go or it will not, and that is the end of it. But if you have to depend upon hundreds of collaborators, and each of them believes that he can do better than any other, life really can be made rather difficult and bitter." '

. . . . .

One day soon after this, Kadereit announced the arrival of Dr. Sternthal to see Ehrlich. Dr. Sternthal was the Health-Councillor (Sanitätsrat) of Braunschweig, and a faithful supporter of Salvarsan since the very first tests were made with it. He reported good curative results among his patients. One case of tabes was especially interesting. Before treatment this patient could only walk painfully with a stick; but after treat-

ment with 606 his physical condition was so amazingly improved that he could jump on to a tram while it was in motion.
A specialist in neurology said about this case that it was 'somewhat better'. On hearing this, Ehrlich remarked with an ironical smile:

'I ask you—somewhat better—and he can jump on to a
moving tram! This is an amazing result!'

Information about improvements and cures came in from
all sides. But in spite of these pleasing results Ehrlich would
not leave Frankfurt. With such an enormous number of patients
undergoing treatment, it was always possible that some unfortunate incident might occur, and he felt that he must constantly be at his post. He did not 'shut off steam' as he had
said he would to his friend Professor Gabriel; and, as always,
he was careless about taking proper meals and had to be
reminded several times to take even the cup of soup for lunch
which Kadereit's wife had prepared for him, but which he
invariably allowed to get cold. There were always many
visitors coming in the afternoon, and every day he seemed to
leave the Institute later, although his wife often telephoned to
him several times to remind him to come home.

Even if he was all ready to leave with his hat and coat on,
he would take them off again if a new visitor arrived, and with
his unfailing kindness would invite the new-comer to sit down.
It is impossible to say how many times he said that to a visitor
during the day, and never could the injunction be followed
because there was really no place to sit on! The visitors therefore always had to remain standing, unless the indefatigable
Kadereit fetched chairs from another room. Ehrlich himself
did not sit down either, of course, and a lengthy conversation,
often lasting an hour or more, took place with everyone
standing all the while.

.   .   .   .   .

Of course, there was still sometimes bad news. The following
is an extract from a letter written to me a long time ago by
Professor Johan Almqvist of Stockholm, one of the first specialists to undertake trial treatments with 606. He visited Ehrlich
in Frankfurt, and, in addition to the many cases in which
successful results had been obtained with Salvarsan, he had
also had to report one case in which the patient had died.

Ehrlich's manner on this occasion evidently made a very deep impression on Professor Almqvist. This is what he wrote:

'It was my first case of death after Salvarsan treatment, caused by encephalitis haemorrhagica interna. I had to tell him every detail of the treatment, the way in which the disease became progressively worse, the result of the post-mortem examination. Although continually interrupted by visitors he always returned to discussion of this particular case, walking up and down his room, at one minute asking animatedly about the details, the next silently meditating. When he finally felt he had found an explanation for the unfortunate alteration in the brain he kept on repeating, as though speaking to himself, still deep in thought:

' "That's the thing, you know . . . *that's* the thing!" '

After that he would not let the matter rest until he had worked out and published a paper calling attention to all the points in the case which had proved fatal, though he was able to tell Dr. Almqvist of a number of similar cases which improved after treatment with 606, which his visitor was able to confirm from his own experience as well.

.   .   .   .   .

Ehrlich's deep sense of responsibility and his invariable custom of following up and discovering the cause of every undesirable incident after treatment with Salvarsan was very widely known, and was once used as a trick by a doctor from Spain in order to secure an interview. He had tried in vain to see Ehrlich, and had been firmly told by Kadereit:

'No, it is really impossible for him to see you to-day.'

But the Spanish doctor was obliged to leave Frankfurt that night, and he had made up his mind to see the great Ehrlich by one means or another. So he took up his position in the long corridor near the door leading to Ehrlich's rooms, and he waited. Presently the great man came out, ready to go home. The visitor introduced himself, saying that he felt he must salute him and offer his congratulations on the great work he had accomplished, although he did not think that Salvarsan would stand the test of time.

'Wieso denn . . . wieso denn?' (How so, what do you mean?)

said Ehrlich and at once began asking him whether he had already tried treatment with Salvarsan himself, whether he had seen unfavourable reactions, what experiences he had had and so on, meanwhile taking the visitor back with him into his laboratory. Having once got inside, the Spanish doctor confessed that he had only used that remark as a pretext in order to see Ehrlich and talk to him, and said that he had had wonderful results with 606 and was very happy to express his great satisfaction. Ehrlich was amused by this trick, and they talked for almost two hours. Finally the enthusiastic Spanish visitor took his leave, having asked for and received a signed photograph of Ehrlich.

.   .   .   .   .

Another little incident showing Ehrlich's kindliness can be mentioned here.

One afternoon, Ehrlich was rummaging in his precious chemical collection, sitting on his heels behind the big laboratory bench, while I was standing on the other side of the bench waiting for his dictation.

All of a sudden, the door leading from the corridor was brusquely opened, and in rushed Dr. Gonder, assistant in the Biological Section of the Speyer-Haus. Before I could warn him he cried out impatiently:

'Well, I must say . . . I have been through all the laboratories looking everywhere and cannot find him! And Kadereit says he isn't in the house. Where's he hiding now?'

Ehrlich, rising from his squatting position, emerged from behind the laboratory bench, with the result that Dr. Gonder stood petrified with an ashen face, unable to utter a word. Ehrlich greeted him amiably:

'Tag ook, lieber Gonder, was gibts Neues?' (Anything new?) and then immediately started talking about some biological observation in which he knew Gonder would be interested. Presently the colour came back into Gonder's face, and he was able to say something in answer to Ehrlich's remarks. Finally, having recovered from his shock, he was able to take a lively part in the conversation, and left the room quite satisfied and happy.

.   .   .   .   .

The Old and the New Salvarsan

Out of all the preparations in the Salvarsan series which were worked out at the Georg Speyer-Haus after the original 606, only No. 914 showed any particular effectiveness in animal experiments. Ehrlich had repeatedly emphasised his doctrine that 'in Chemotherapy *hundreds* of preparations must be made and tried out'; and No. 914, more than three hundred numbers after 606, is a proof of it.

After the first discovery of its usefulness in animals, further long series of animal experiments had to be made in order to determine the tolerated dose and the curative activity of the new substance, and set up a standard for it. Then again, trial treatments with human patients had to be undertaken by a number of the most experienced physicians in clinics and in private practice. From all quarters came reports that No. 914 —called 'Neosalvarsan'—had not such strong curative powers as the original 606, the 'Old Salvarsan'. But in spite of this less powerful effect there were, after the publication in the medical journals of the tests carried out on animals and human patients, many doctors who were strongly in favour of replacing the original Salvarsan in general practice by Neosalvarsan, because the latter was more easily soluble than the original 606 which was difficult to handle. With Neosalvarsan the work of the physician would be made much easier. This opinion on the part of the doctors was supported by the chemical works; for the manufacture of 914 was also much easier than that of 606, and did not require such difficult and elaborate precautions, especially in the intermediate stages of production, as did the original 606.

It was hard for Ehrlich to give his consent to this. His chief aim and desire was the 'therapia sterilisans magna', that is, curing with a single injection if possible. With the original Salvarsan this was attained in many cases: not only in the dangerous disease in horses 'Brustseuche' (pleurisy), and the dreaded tropical disease Framboesia or 'Yaws', but also in syphilis, where incredible results were often obtained with single injections of strong doses, up to 0·9 g. But Ehrlich had to yield. He made this concession to the doctors under the stress of circumstances, but with a sad heart and mind.

It was a compromise. The introduction of Salvarsan brought about a complete revolution in the treatment of syphilis, that terrible and dreaded disease which everyone avoided mentioning and which was never discussed in public until the invention of Salvarsan. But with the new treatment, physicians and the entire medical world were faced with a number of new and difficult tasks. Ehrlich's instructions concerning the selection of cases to be treated; his stipulations about the doses to be given, the correct making up of solutions, and the precautions to be observed when giving the injections—all these had to be studied. There was also the control and observation of the patient after the injection, and all this was so entirely new and overwhelming and carried with it so much responsibility that Ehrlich could not refuse to comply with the appeals of those concerned to facilitate their work by replacing the original Salvarsan by Neosalvarsan. All that the modern medical practitioner of to-day regards as quite natural in the treatment of syphilis, all the necessary measures which are daily carried out so easily, as a matter of course, required at that time a particular study and special training. Intravenous injection, which Ehrlich demanded categorically after so much mischief had been done with intramuscular and subcutaneous injections, had until then been used only in cases of the utmost emergency. It had to be learned and practised, and the great reluctance which existed about using it generally had to be overcome. It is largely owing to Ehrlich's energetic measures that the intravenous injection is now used by every medical practitioner.

Quite a number of those doctors who had done good work with the original Salvarsan, and were satisfied with the results, remained faithful to the old 606 in spite of everything, even after the new 914 had generally replaced it. There were even more daring ones who boldly used tap water for their solutions instead of freshly distilled or sterilised water. They often escaped without any disagreeable results after treatment, and apparently cured their patients with a single injection of 0·9 g.

No one who knew Ehrlich can doubt that if only he had lived a few years longer, and had continued to watch over the treatment with his immense energy and profound sense of responsibility, he would have insisted on the re-introduction of the original 606, or perhaps another even stronger form of Salvarsan which might have been developed in further chemical experiments. And he would have succeeded in this demand as soon as the requirements of the new therapy had been mastered by the doctors who were to use it.

During the years which followed, when it was in general use for human patients, Ehrlich was often asked to give lectures on Salvarsan by the leaders of various important societies concerning themselves with the enlightenment of the public about venereal diseases. These societies of laymen, and also the great Health Insurance Societies, felt that it was important that their members should know about these diseases and the new treatment, and they naturally hoped to get Ehrlich himself to lecture on this subject on which he was such an authority. He fully realised the great ethical value of making such information public, and hardly any other man in his position would have refrained from making use of such opportunities of speaking to large gatherings of laymen. But he always refused such invitations on principle, for he would not lay himself open to the possible reproach that he was speaking in order to advertise himself and his specific. Even his friends who tried to persuade him could not make him change his mind. I give here one of the letters of refusal, because it is characteristic of Ehrlich's way of thinking, and shows his great modesty.

On 8 June, 1912, he wrote to the Free Union of Health Insurance Societies of the Province of Brandenburg in Berlin:

'Thank you very much for your kind invitation to give a lecture on Salvarsan treatment before the 8th Provincial Conference of the Health Insurance Union of the Province of Brandenburg. I should have complied with this request with pleasure if I were not obliged to refuse it as a matter of principle. For the same reasons I have not been able to grant the same request made to me by the Secretary of the Frankfurt Society for Health Insurance, Herr Graef, with whom I think you are well acquainted. He is also a believer in Salvarsan therapy.

'Firstly it is the fact that I have not a medical practice which makes me refuse. And secondly I fear that such a lecture by me might be taken advantage of by my enemies, and there are many of them I am sorry to say. If I deliver such a lecture my adversaries will say: "It is not surprising that Ehrlich, the

Q

inventor of the remedy, is in favour of it!" The evil-minded might perhaps add as well: "He feels that it is necessary to make propaganda for it!" '

.   .   .   .   .

Demonstration of Spirochaeta Pallida in the Brain and Spinal-Marrow of Cases of General Paralysis and Tabes

Professor Noguchi, of the Rockefeller Institute for Medical Research in New York, came to Frankfurt on 10 February, 1914, to see Ehrlich and report to him the results of his important experiments bearing upon the treatment of Parasyphilis (General Paralysis and Tabes).

By impregnating with nitrate of silver certain preparations of brain and spinal cord, from patients with general paralysis and tabes, Professor Noguchi had discovered an indisputable fact which hitherto it had been impossible to prove with any other method of staining. This was that the spirochaeta pallida, the germ causing syphilis, really penetrates into the brain and the spinal cord and there causes the terrible ravages which many investigators had declared must be an *indirect* consequence of the disease, since no proof of the presence of the germs in these places could previously be obtained in any way.

During this visit, Professor Noguchi gave a demonstration of his experiments and findings in the packed lecture hall of the Medical Clinic at Frankfurt University, before the Medical Faculty of the University, the students and all the physicians of the city. He concluded his lecture with these words:

'With the discovery of the *spirochaeta pallida* in cases of so-called parasyphilis, dawn begins to break upon this gigantic problem of treatment. In Salvarsan and Neosalvarsan we have a most powerful weapon to hand against the well-known forms of primary and secondary syphilis, caused by this organism; and we can banish the demon with more force than ever before. Is it too much to hope, after such great results in research work have already been achieved, that Ehrlich's genius will once more show us the ways and means leading to a therapeutic conquest of this special form of syphilitic disease —this disease which has done such immense harm to humanity, and against which we have hitherto been completely helpless?'

'What a landmark in the history of medicine! What an historic occasion!' was the remark heard on all sides after this demonstration, which made a deep impression. The assembled crowd of listeners were able to convince themselves of the fact that the *spirochaeta pallida* really was present in the brain and spinal cord of parasyphilitic patients, both from the specimen seen in the lecture hall and by going over to the Georg Speyer-Haus and examining preparations under the microscope. There I overheard Ehrlich saying, rather excitedly, about one of the visitors:

'Der ungeschickte Taperkerl sieht nichts!' (That uncapable good-for-nothing sees nothing!) 'He cannot even see properly although the spirochaetes are lying in the preparations in heaps!'

Evidently some one in the audience at the lecture was not very expert in the use of the microscope!

About this time Ehrlich ceased to deliver lectures. Instead he occupied his time replying to urgent requests from colleagues asking for information and advice on the use of Salvarsan. All the time also he was carrying out experiments to improve the technique and avoid complications.

All through the long years of research undertaken by him since his first paper 'Contributions to the knowledge of staining with aniline dyes and their use in microscopical technique' at the age of twenty-three, up to the last findings in chemistry, he had poured out papers and given lectures at important congresses in Germany and abroad. In this way he acquired many devoted followers who were introduced to his mode of thinking and guided step by step to an understanding of the scientific advances made by him. His articles and lectures constantly brought to light something new and essential to science. His addresses in foreign countries were always held on special occasions and brought knowledge and enlightenment to a multitude of listeners.

In 1899 at the Lister Institute he gave an exposé on his findings 'The Constitution of Diphtheria Toxins' which was most helpful to his English-speaking colleagues. This was published in the Transactions of the Institute. In March 1900 he delivered the famous 'Croonian Lecture' before the Royal Society 'On Immunity with special reference to cell life'. At this address he demonstrated for the first time his idea of the 'Side-Chain' theory.

In the same year, August 1900, he lectured at the XIIIth International Congress of Medicine in Paris on 'Leucocytose'; and in 1903 in Brussels at the XIIIth International Congress of Hygiene and Demography on 'The best methods of measuring the activity of Sera'. In 1904 he came again to London to the XVth Convocation of the University and spoke in the Kent Theatre on 'The binding conditions between Toxin and Antitoxin', and in 1907 he delivered the 'Harben Lectures' of the Royal Institute of Public Health, London, comprising three lectures: (1) 'On Immunity with special reference to the relations existing between the distribution and the action of Antigens'; (2) 'On the Athreptic Function'; (3) 'Chemotherapeutic Studies on Trypanosomes'.

When he was made Nobel Laureate of 1908 on account of his Research Work on Immunity (conjointly with Professor Metchnikoff of the Institut Pasteur in Paris), he lectured (in December 1908) before the Nobel Committee in Stockholm on 'Partial Functions of the Cell'.

At the 27th Congress of Internal Medicine in Wiesbaden on April 19th, 1910, Ehrlich announced officially his invention of 606, and at the 82nd Session of the German Physicians and Investigators of Natural Science in Königsberg, October 1910, reported on six months of treatment of syphilis with dioxydiamino-arseno-benzene (606). Other congresses followed in 1911 and 1912. In 1913 he visited London for the last time. There at the XVIIth International Congress of Medicine in August he gave two lectures, 'Chemotherapy' and 'Treatment of Syphilis with Salvarsan and Related Substances'. These still live in the memory of many who were present. It is reported that when Ehrlich appeared at the lecture theatre he was greeted enthusiastically, and at the end of each lecture there was thunderous applause enough to raise the roof of the big Congress Hall.

CHAPTER XXII

EHRLICH'S SIXTIETH BIRTHDAY

On 14 March, 1914, Ehrlich celebrated his sixtieth birthday. All the daily papers had long articles about him and his wonderful work. Some of them issued richly illustrated special numbers in his honour. The medical, chemical and natural science periodicals also celebrated the occasion, praising Ehrlich and all that he had done for the promotion of science and the benefit of mankind.

Professor Metchnikoff and Professor Roux of the Pasteur Institute, Paris, wrote the following in an article on the occasion:

'L'ensemble du personnage est aussi sympathique qu'intéressant. Inépuisable fournisseur d'idées directrices, Ehrlich est un des maîtres qui comptes de plus d'élèves, tous lui restent attachés, car il est en même temps le plus affable des hommes.'

Telegrams and letters arrived by the hundred from every country, and many of his friends from abroad came to take part in the simple friendly celebration. A real holiday mood prevailed, and the two reception rooms in Ehrlich's house were hardly big enough to hold all those who had come, his friends, collaborators, assistants and former pupils. The latter had compiled a special book on his work, a bulky volume of 668 pages,[1] and its solemn presentation was an important part of the ceremony. Dr. Arthur von Weinberg, a helpful and appreciative friend of Ehrlich's for many years, Professor Sachs, Professor Max Neisser and Professor Morgenroth were some of the most prominent guests. Professor Morgenroth had come from Berlin, where he was working on Chemotherapy most successfully with Ehrlich's methods. All Ehrlich's family and near relatives were there to honour him, his cousin Felix Pinkus from Berlin and many others. From the two Ehrlich Institutes

---

[1] 'Paul Ehrlich: Eine Darstellung seines wissenschaftlichen Wirkens', *loc. cit.*

there were all the collaborators and assistants, three of the women laboratory assistants, Kadereit and myself.

During the festivities Dr. von Weinberg announced that, in accordance with his suggestions, the friends and pupils of Ehrlich planned to found a new wing at the Serum Institute as a present to Ehrlich, with a large laboratory completely equipped in the most up-to-date way. Adjoining it there would be a pleasant study where he could work and also receive visitors, with a large writing-desk, arm-chairs and bookcases, and also an office for me. The work was already in hand and would incorporate Ehrlich's own special wishes and be completed in the very near future. Then, as well as having better working conditions, Ehrlich would be able to attend to his daily work with a little more comfort and in rooms more suited to his position.

Deeply touched by this generous gift, Ehrlich shook hands all round and had a few kindly words for everyone. He much preferred this simple gathering in his own home to a large official ceremony; for, as we know, he was no lover of public receptions.

Ehrlich, of course, stayed on in his old rooms for some time, as the new wing was not yet finished. When the equipment was being installed and the new laboratory was almost ready, the furniture for the new reception room was delivered and Ehrlich went over once to watch and see what it was all going to look like. Then, taking a deep breath, he returned to his old set of rooms, which he loved and where he was happy to work. He could not make up his mind to see to any preparations for moving into the new rooms.

· · · · ·

Recollections from Youth

One afternoon a visitor came whom Ehrlich was especially glad to welcome. This was Dr. Meyer, who had by this time been a physician in Hamburg for many years. He was about ten years younger than Ehrlich, and they had been friends since they were children. When Meyer was a little boy of seven, Ehrlich had been a student of seventeen at the Breslau College, and much loved and admired by the other boys. They had played together during the holidays with the boys of

Strehlen, and later he had worked with Ehrlich as his assistant in Berlin.

Ehrlich and Meyer both stood in Ehrlich's room while they talked, for as usual the only available chair was Ehrlich's own. They smoked and talked very animatedly, as old friends do when they meet again.

'You know, I have always watched your doings ever since I was a child,' said Meyer to Ehrlich. 'I have always been most impressed by the amount of work you have done, in spite of the fact that at school and college you were often a bit of a trial!'

Ehrlich tapped him on the arm with a mischievous laugh:

'Ja natürlich, natürlich' (yes, indeed, indeed). 'You must remember that laziness is only an outlet, a regulator of the working brain. If I had not been given to loafing about and neglecting my work then—and afterwards too—wissen Sie, verstehen Sie—during the "Bohemian period" of youth—with "floods" of beer—in clouds of cigar-smoke—with amusements and recreations—"need of oxygen of the organism"—you know. . . . I should long ago have found myself in a lunatic asylum.'

Meyer laughed heartily. 'Do you remember that time at College when you wore your summer overcoat all the winter because you could not find your winter one?' he asked. 'And then in the end it was found in the lecture room where it had been hanging all the time!'

Ehrlich burst out laughing at this memory of his youth.

'And then,' continued Meyer, 'when we were working together in Berlin, I was always filled with admiration at the way you would suddenly abandon a particular line of work if you saw that nothing would come of it; and you would immediately begin something fresh. What struck me as more wonderful than anything else was the way in which you always foresaw what was later on proved to be true. There is absolutely no one to equal you in that!'

Ehrlich stood there with a reminiscent smile on his face.

Finally he said:

'Yes . . . we must work upon what is *going to be* of real value and interest, not upon what is *already* in existence. And it is important—*eo ipso*—that we should not continue to work in one particular field of investigation until it is exhausted. We must go on further and leave some of the harvest for others to gather as well.'

Meyer nodded. 'Indeed you have always done that,' he said. 'And what a lot of people have benefited from it!'

'Above all,' Ehrlich continued, referring to his favourite formula, 'for successful work there must always be what I call the four big "Gs": Geduld, Geschick, Geld and Glück.' (Patience, ability, money and luck.)

'If the first three are present and used properly, the fourth "G" comes by itself,' declared Meyer emphatically.

Ehrlich was absorbed in thought.

'With a thousand masts I went out on to the ocean of discovery,' he mused, smiling slightly.

'They have not been in vain,' replied Meyer, his voice full of admiration. 'All these titanic, heaven-assailing theories of yours which have turned out to be right and revolutionised the whole of medicine. . . .'

'So it appears, my dear friend,' remarked Ehrlich with a laugh. 'Evidently I was not such a silly ass in those days as I seemed!'

.   .   .   .   .

Ehrlich had a deep-rooted intuitive feeling which made him at once trust some people with whom he came in contact, while there were others in whom he could never put implicit confidence. With his optimism and frankness he made friends easily, and for this reason he was sometimes disappointed, even in cases where he thought he could depend upon a firm and long-standing friendship. Once, after his invention of 606, when admiration, glory and distinctions were being showered on him from all sides, he confessed to me that he was deeply hurt after a visit from one of the dearest friends of his youth.

'Even *he* is full of envy and grudges me my success,' he said. And this friend was himself a scientist in whose life honours and appreciation had been plentiful.

When anything happened to make Ehrlich doubtful about the trustworthiness of a friend, the good relations between them might be superficially patched up after a quarrel; but a rent in the friendship remained, and the old trusting faith, which he could bestow so generously on his friends, would not return. Such disappointments were a source of great sorrow to him.

CHAPTER XXIII

HONOURS AND APPRECIATION

A GREAT number of honours and distinctions were bestowed on Ehrlich, especially during the last years of his life. After the invention and introduction of 606 his merits were recognised everywhere, and innumerable scientific societies in many countries appointed him an honorary member. Universities in foreign countries and in Germany gave him the degree of Doctor *honoris causa*. He received a multitude of decorations, the Prussian Government made him a Right Honourable Privy Councillor (Wirklicher Geheimrat) with the title of Excellency (Excellenz). The street in which his Institutes were situated, so long called Sandhofstrasse, was named 'Paul Ehrlich-Strasse' in his honour and he was made a Freeman of the City of Frankfurt. Naturally all this pleased him, though he did not attach undue importance to it. What really gave him great and heartfelt pleasure was being appointed to the very exclusive Honorary Membership of the 'Deutsche Chemische Gesellschaft' (German Chemical Society); for this was an honour bestowed only upon those engaged in chemical research as a profession.

What also made Ehrlich really happy was the first simple postcard he received from a cured patient. He kept this always in his wallet in the breast pocket of his coat.

Another equally great source of pleasure to Ehrlich was the correspondence he had with Professor Emil Fischer, the world-famous chemist, and the appreciation he received from him.

One afternoon Kadereit announced a visitor and whispered something to Ehrlich. Delightedly Ehrlich exclaimed with excitement:

'Really? Is he really here?' and ran out at once into the corridor. At Kadereit's door a white-haired old gentleman was waiting, and Ehrlich hurried to greet him. It was Emil Fischer. Deeply touched by this visit, Ehrlich called out:

'Fancy *you* coming to see me. . . .'

'But, my dear friend,' interrupted Emil Fischer, laughing, 'of course I must come to see our great Ehrlich—Honorary Member of the German Chemical Society—at work in his own surroundings! What new and staggering discovery have you got to tell me about? Does not something like that happen every day with you?'

'I really have two wonderful surprises to-day,' replied Ehr-

Professor Emil Fischer, Chairman of the Deutsche Chemische Gesellschaft, Berlin. (German Chemical Society)

lich with a smile. 'From several different quarters I have heard that the "Brustseuche der Pferde" (Pleurisy in horses), which hitherto has been incurable, can now be cured with a single injection of Salvarsan!' His voice rose with excitement.

'But that really *is* a wonderful surprise!' said Professor Fischer. 'It will effect a very great saving. And can we really say that with a single injection this terrible disease in horses will become a harmless sickness?'

Ehrlich nodded and said:

'The therapia sterilisans magna . . . the goal at which I am always aiming! With human patients, of course, with syphilitic cases, it will not be attained so easily. But we shall see. The second surprise is this: Dr. Baermann writes to me from the Dutch East Indies that in one of the hospitals there all the natives suffering from Framboesia—Yaws—you know—that frightful tropical disease in which the whole body is covered with ulcers looking like strawberries. . . .'

'Yes,' said Emil Fischer, nodding, and looking at Ehrlich with great attention, 'that is why it is called strawberry-sickness. . . .'

'Wissen Sie, verstehen Sie,' went on Ehrlich, 'they have all been cured with one injection. All,' he repeated, his voice raised, '*all*, with a single injection, *cured*!'

'Miraculous!' exclaimed Professor Fischer.

'Dr. Baermann writes, saying: "The Hospital could be closed"! And Hata, who has gone back to Tokio, wissen Sie, verstehen Sie, he writes almost at the same time exactly the same thing about a Japanese hospital. There they have held great celebrations to which Hata was invited. The children performed dances with music and sang folk songs. Hata says in his letter: "I shed tears, I was so moved." '

Ehrlich and Fischer were both smiling. Then Professor Fischer put his hand on Ehrlich's shoulder and said:

'Go on like that, my dear Ehrlich! If *one* human being deserves success, it is you!'

When he left, Ehrlich accompanied Professor Fischer to the steps leading out from the Institute. Returning to his room after saying good-bye to his visitor he was deep in thought, with a far-away look in his eyes, absent-mindedly swinging his spectacles by one of the sidepieces. After great praise from a famous man like this, Ehrlich was always deeply moved. It made him as shy as a child.

.   .   .   .   .

Soon afterwards a man and his wife knocked at Kadereit's door. They were evidently foreigners, and were dressed with dignified solemnity in black. Kadereit opened the door and they spoke to him in low tones. He shrugged his shoulders, and with an expression of importance on his face said:

'I do not think that will be possible to-day.'

'But we *must* see the Professor,' they insisted together. 'We have come all the way from Russia, specially to *see him*!'

'Very well then, I will find out,' said Kadereit, going towards Ehrlich's door. When he came in he said:

'There are two Russian actors here, Herr Jeheimrat, a man and his wife, who are terribly anxious to see you, and refuse to be sent away!'

Ehrlich was tired and wanting to go home. 'But it is so late already!' he complained.

'I know,' said Kadereit despairingly. 'But they are patients, and they only want just to say good-day to you.'

'Then let them come,' said Ehrlich, taking off his hat again.

They had hardly entered the room when the woman rushed forward sobbing and threw herself at his feet, clinging to his knees and covering his hands with kisses. Her husband stood gravely behind her, his head bent down in profound respect. Ehrlich though deeply moved was embarrassed by this demonstration and tried to restrain and comfort the lady, saying:

'But please, you must not distress yourself, I beg you!'

At length she grew calmer and, assisted by her husband, though still hesitant and with much emotion, told their story. They had both been members of a Russian theatre. Then her husband became very ill with spinal syphilis and was unable to play. Unemployment, suffering and distress followed. At last he had obtained treatment with 606—was completely cured—and was already able to return to work. Tears of thankfulness and gratitude came again as she told her story of how Ehrlich's treatment had saved him, and their despair and fear were banished.

Deeply moved, Ehrlich warned them, kindly and modestly, that they must not be too sure of a really permanent cure as this was difficult to obtain in long-standing cases of the disease. It was necessary for the patient to remain for some time under the control of his doctor. But their overwhelming gratitude was undiminished, and after they had departed, full of happiness at having seen and thanked the great Ehrlich in person, he said to me, quite embarrassed:

'These Russians, they really are extraordinarily passionate creatures, aren't they?'

I could only agree, feeling also quite upset by the touching scene I had just witnessed. The visit of these people made a very great impression on me, for it showed again, as so often before, the great goodness, kindliness and modesty of Ehrlich's character.

CHAPTER XXIV

SLANDER AND LIBEL

As has already been shown, Ehrlich's invention received an enormous amount of publicity after the Congress of Internal Medicine at Wiesbaden in April 1910. The daily papers seized on it, and reported everything they could about it, including much that was not true. The publicity was very distasteful to Ehrlich, but he was powerless to prevent it, especially as every moment of his day was filled with work. One small local paper in Frankfurt glorified him in a most extravagant way both in prose and verse. This also vexed Ehrlich very much, and he called it impudent and bad mannered. His enemies, however, took advantage of these exaggerated accounts to slander, equally wildly, not only Salvarsan but Ehrlich himself. They stopped at nothing. We can imagine how deeply hurt Ehrlich was when a question was asked in the Prussian Diet based on these libellous attacks and information obtained from malicious and evil sources.

What was even worse was that some physicians, being accustomed before the invention of Salvarsan to treating their syphilitic patients for the rest of their lives, thought that by curing them in a short time with 606 they would make far less money out of them. In consequence they were hostile to the new specific and abused it without sense or reason. They even supported the attacks made in another local Frankfurt paper.

Ehrlich's sensitive mind suffered greatly from all this libellous abuse, and the mental distress which it caused him reacted unfavourably on his physical health. He was always ready at any time to take up and discuss criticism based on a sound and reasonable foundation, but these scurrilous attacks, unsupported by any evidence, were too heavy a burden for him to bear.

In letters to his friends, Ehrlich often mentioned this. He wrote that he only wanted to do the best he could, and he felt it was a shame that a handful of people opposed to inoculation and all medical treatment, people who wished to cure every disease with 'natural' remedies, and people completely ignorant about his work, should be able to attack it and him in such a completely unscientific and prejudiced way.

These attacks went on for a long time. One particular instance which occurred early in 1914 should be recorded in detail here.

There was always a lot of bustle and traffic and people going to and fro in the centre of Frankfurt, around the old 'Hauptwache' with the Schillerplatz and the Schiller statue, and the streets called the Rossmarkt and the Zeil. Every day in and around the Café Hauptwache could be seen a strange looking man, dressed in a rough dark brown monk's habit, with a rope round his waist. He went to and fro from one table to another, went into the café and out again into the street, and back again. Under his arm he carried a pile of copies of his own local newspaper, all of which he wrote, corrected and printed and even sold himself. As he offered it to the passers-by and the patrons of the café he called out:

'Die Wahrheit! Die Wahrheit!' (The Truth! The Truth!) 'Sensational revelations about 606 at Frankfurt Hospital. . . .'

This strange man was Karl Wassmann, who believed in curing all diseases by Nature alone. He was clean-shaven, with black hair and dark eyes which had that strangely fascinating, almost hypnotising, expression often found in mentally abnormal people. He did not behave awkwardly as so many psychopathic people do, but on the contrary had quite pleasant manners and was not at all disagreeable in appearance. He had a curl of hair which was always falling over his forehead and which he would push back with a flick of his fingers. Everybody laughed at him and nobody took him seriously. But they bought his fantastic paper with its huge title *The Truth*, just for a love of sensation.

I once saw this queer creature in a Frankfurt tram, without knowing that it was Karl Wassmann. He was dressed in an ordinary dark suit, with a very high stiff collar, a broad black cravat such as was worn about a hundred years earlier, and a short light-coloured overcoat beneath which showed the jacket of his suit. On this occasion he had a small black moustache. When paying for his ticket he attracted the attention of everyone in the tram by having a lively conversation with the conductor, making himself very agreeable to him; and when the conductor was giving him change he gave him a generous tip, for which the conductor thanked him profusely. Wassmann spoke in a strange deep, clear, slightly vibrating voice, and evidently liked hearing himself talk and making everyone else notice him. Then he looked at all the other passengers, one by one, with a fixed and penetrating stare. But before his glance reached the far corner where I was sitting I was overcome by a sudden inexplicable feeling of uneasiness so strong that I got out of the tram at the next stop, although I had not yet reached my home. It is well known that psychopaths like Wassmann do often have a strange effect upon other people.

Wassmann launched violent attacks in his paper against Ehrlich, against 606, and against the Frankfurt Hospital where, he asserted, the unfortunate patients were 'forced' to undergo treatment and 'dragged to the injections' against their will. He wrote about 'monstrous incidents' which he alleged occurred after the injections, and abused Ehrlich himself.

In spite of warnings and advice from Ehrlich and others that he should not pay any attention to these shameless attacks, Professor Herxheimer, Director of the Dermatological Section of Frankfurt Hospital, refused to put up with it and began legal proceedings in a libel action against Karl Wassmann. He said this was really necessary, because there were a number of physicians who were influenced by Wassmann's defamation of 606.

Ehrlich had to be called as an expert witness during the hearing of this action, which took place in May 1914 before the Frankfurt Court of Justice. The fact that he had to appear in the Court and was, after all, involved in this unpleasant affair, caused him much unhappiness. Everyone who saw him at that time was alarmed about his health. He felt it to be, as he expressed it himself, 'the worst shame of my life, to be confronted with such a person'. He was always ready to discuss responsible criticism with his colleagues and other experts, and to endeavour to overcome their objections to his views with scientific reasoning and proofs of his experiments. But he knew that arguing with such mentally unbalanced people as Karl Wassmann was utterly impossible.

Ehrlich's friends and colleagues who were present at the hearing said afterwards that, as he replied to the questions put by the President of the Court, his face was pale and sorrowful, and he could only control his feelings with a very great effort. They all believed that having been involved in this action had a very serious affect on Ehrlich's physical condition, and that his death, not much more than a year later, was partly due to the distress which it caused him and which weighed so heavily on his sensitive spirit.

When questioned about 'disagreeable incidents' after treatment at the Hospital, such as transfixion of the vein into which the injection should have been made, with resulting inflammation, Ehrlich could only reply that when the treatment was first started this had occurred unfortunately in other places also, but that, as the technique of the intravenous injection was perfected and the skill and experience of the doctors in giving it increased, this difficulty had soon been overcome. He also said that he had always had, and still had, absolute confidence in Professor Herxheimer and his assistants. Furthermore, on this occasion, as always, he affirmed that he had always wanted to do the very best for the patients and was ready and able, at any time, to discuss any doubts or criticisms if they were based on a scientific foundation.

It is not known whether the prostitutes, who had given money to Wassmann for writing his libellous articles, and who were heard during the action, were charged with bribery and slander. At any rate no verdict was given against them. In answer to their assertions that they had been 'forced' to undergo treatment with 606, Professor Herxheimer and his assistants and other witnesses said that these patients were not co-operative and that it had sometimes been necessary to use a certain amount of 'pressure'. Outweighing this there was the enormous number of other patients who had also been treated and cured with 606 and who were extremely grateful to the doctors and to Ehrlich.

I do not know whether Wassmann appeared in Court with a moustache and in the dark suit, stiff collar, black tie and light overcoat; or whether he was clean-shaven and in his monk's dress with sandals and a rope girdle. I was not present and can only report what Ehrlich's friends who were there have told

R

me. But I am sure that Wassmann acted with theatrical gestures and empty phrases. He was found guilty of libel, and of
taking money from the prostitute patients and writing his
infamous articles at their instigation. He was sentenced to a
year's imprisonment. The Frankfurt daily papers reported
nothing about the action except the verdict, and newspapers
outside Frankfurt gave it no mention at all. As it happened,
Wassmann stayed barely two months in prison, for he came
under the amnesty declared at the outbreak of the First World
War. He did not mention 606 any more, changed the name of
his paper to *Love*, and devoted it to other ends.

CHAPTER XXV

THE FINAL YEAR

I SHALL never forget the commotion there was at the end of July 1914 when the war broke out. Special editions of the newspapers with enormous headlines . . . crowds of people round the news-stands . . . some sceptical looking, some sad, some pugnacious . . . marching men everywhere . . . endless goings to and fro, to and fro.

In the Serum Institute, in the street formerly known as Sandhofstrasse, but since Ehrlich's sixtieth birthday in March 1914 renamed 'Paul Ehrlich-Strasse', was also a scene of great activity. Immediately war broke out a great speed-up began; there was a breathless rush and a terrific amount of work to be done preparing serum for the Army on a huge scale. This had priority over all other work. Every room was used for this work, and every worker.

Ehrlich's new laboratory, which he had only been to look at once and never worked in, was requisitioned by the military authorities and was immediately commandeered as a control centre for all the sera which the chemical works now had to produce in large quantities. In the new reception room, and in my new office which had not yet been furnished, were piled cases and chests filled with sera ready for use, waiting to be dispatched after being checked through the control centre. Ehrlich had never really liked the idea of leaving his old rooms and moving to these new surroundings. It seems as if he may have had a presentiment that he would never work there.

Very exhausted from overwork and depressed by the continued attacks of his enemies, he had at last gone to Baden-Baden for a holiday. But at the outbreak of war he returned to Frankfurt immediately. I shall never forget the distressed look on his face as he put his hands to his head and cried out:

'But this war is pure madness! No good can possibly come of it!'

Ehrlich felt quite lost and strange in the noisy bustle of the

R*

Institute in war-time, with people running hither and thither, and large cases continually being dragged along the corridors ready to be transported to the Army. Only in his old laboratory, and in his study with all the old piles of books, could he find a refuge and a quiet place in which to think.

His staff had planned to take advantage of his absence on holiday to move to the new laboratory all the innumerable bottles containing his precious collection of the rare chemical substances which he had had specially prepared for him. But before he left he heard of this plan, and very decidedly protested.

'In my absence nothing is to be touched,' he had said. 'I want to take care of all that myself.' And of course the Laboratory Assistant, Goeldner, had to obey. This was a very good thing, for if the plan had been carried out he would not have been able to find anything on his return. He would not have been able to work in the new laboratory, and the old one would have been emptied. It is impossible to imagine how unhappy he would have been. Only once or twice did he go into the new wing to see what they were doing there. I can always see how desolate he seemed as he returned from it, walking slowly down the long corridor into his old rooms, deep in thought, closing the door behind him with resignation.

Almost to the last moment of his life he went on working for the improvement of Salvarsan, rummaging in his chemical collection, making test tube experiments. He also gave much attention to the cancer experiments which were going on in the Cancer Section of the Institute. As a result of long years of study and experiment, Ehrlich had come to the conclusion that cancer was not of bacterial origin, as some scientists had believed, but was due to an excessive, uncontrolled growth and multiplication of cells, the cause of which was to be sought in other directions. At the time of his death these experiments were in full swing. Unfortunately soon afterwards Professor Apolant, the head of the Cancer Section, died of an affection of the heart.

There were many changes in the Georg Speyer-Haus as well as in the Serum Institute as a result of the war, especially through the call-up for military service. Dr. Bertheim was summoned to his cavalry corps at once, and going down the stairs of the house in Berlin where he was billeted caught his spurs in the carpet and fell, fracturing his skull and dying instantly.

Shortly before the outbreak of war, Ehrlich had invited the young and talented chemical research worker Dr. Paul Karrer to come over and join him from Zürich. A very interesting and

*Dr. Paul Karrer, Chemical Assistant at the
Georg Speyer-Haus*

satisfactory collaboration developed between them, and they became fast friends. Ehrlich was able to discuss with Dr. Karrer all his test tube experiments, and entrusted to him the detailed working out of his ideas. During this time some articles about Silver-Salvarsan were published. In 1939 this same Professor Karrer, back in Zürich, was awarded the Nobel Prize for Chemistry for 1938.

News came over from England, in spite of the war, about

the work of a former pupil of Ehrlich's, Dr. Carl Browning of Glasgow, and it pleased him very much. Dr. Browning, after returning home some years before the war, had continued experiments with trypan dyes which he had begun when working in Ehrlich's Institute as his assistant. Dr. Browning found that a particular yellow dye 'Trypaflavin' [1] was very effective in disinfecting and healing serious wounds. This discovery was followed up in the British Army Medical Service, and experiments were made on a large scale. Valuable results were thus obtained, especially with regard to the rapid healing of the edges of wounds.

About the difficulties of disinfection Ehrlich once said:

'When the task of sterilising a room first arose, it was only possible to find a reliable solution after long years of experiments. Naturally this task would be still more difficult if the room to be sterilised were not empty but full of material of all kinds. And if it were stated that the contents and walls of the room consisted of living material, and that the destruction of the parasites must be done without damage to the living contents of the room, the task would be considered an impossible one.

'In spite of this, the task can be done in the case of trypanosomes—can be solved in a simple manner by a single injection with doses which are practically without danger to the animal. This would be an ideal treatment, the "*therapia magna sterilisans.*"

'Work in this field is, however, so complicated and difficult that it is impossible to rush on with the speed of an express train. We must be satisfied if on the whole a gradual progress can be made. At the very beginning of my chemotherapeutical studies, when my collaborators were often discouraged on account of the monotony of the work and the slow progress, I comforted them again and again, saying that they must consider how very small our progress has been in the course of the previous *centuries*!'

.   .   .   .   .

During the first year of the War—the last of his life—Ehrlich's health grew worse and he had to follow strict medical advice especially with regard to diet. Long years of heavy

---

[1] The now well-known and widely used Acriflavine.

smoking of too strong cigars, irregular meals, in fact, almost complete disregard of proper food—these things had combined to produce a disastrous effect on his system. He was ordered to give up smoking, and this he found very hard, although he always pretended that leaving off a habit was really not difficult.

He had never before taken time during the day to have a proper meal, and he considered it a great burden to have to do so now and to be obliged to take such care of his body and see that he had the right number of calories, etc. He suffered from a complete lack of appetite, so it was, as he wrote to friends during that year, 'an absolute torture' to take the prescribed amount of nourishment. However, he knew that it was necessary and he tried to do the best he could.

During his visit to the United States he had first come across the grapefruit, which at that time was almost exclusively grown in Florida and California, and he had enjoyed it very much as an appetiser. After the outbreak of war when there could be no imports from foreign countries, it was impossible to get this fruit anywhere. At length someone told him that grapefruit were also grown in Italy. Accordingly he wrote to his former pupil and friend Professor Maurizio Ascoli, in Catania, asking him to get some and send them to him if possible. After many inquiries and much searching, Professor Ascoli succeeded in finding the one place in Italy where grapefruit were being grown at that time. Ehrlich was overjoyed, and when sending his thanks to Professor Ascoli he apologised for the trouble he had caused him by the search. This is what he wrote to his friend:

'Now you really have succeeded in tracing the only person in Europe who has grapefruit and have made him send me all that he has left in his possession—eleven of them. They have arrived here, a light lemon colour, in perfect condition and they taste exquisite. Perhaps it is very foolish to attach so much importance to such a little passion, but if one is always without appetite longings "*quasimodo gravida*" will develop and one sets one's heart upon them!'

But his health did not improve. When, about Christmas 1914, he had a slight stroke, it was the first serious warning, although he recovered from the obvious effects of this mild attack in a few days. His grave illness progressed imperceptibly, without giving him or those around him any suspicion that catastrophe was near. All he said in letters to his friends was that he did not 'feel as fresh as usual'.

Only a short time before the war Ehrlich had at last been persuaded to buy a car so that he could travel more comfortably between his home and the Institutes. At the outbreak of war the car was immediately requisitioned by the military

*Last photograph taken of Ehrlich, in 1914, a
year before his death*

authorities, and Ehrlich had to go back to his old custom of using a horse-drawn cab.

During the last year of his life I used to call for him at his house every morning to accompany him to the Institutes. Often, especially in the spring and summer when the weather was fine, we would drive only as far as the Hippodrome riding-school where the Paul Ehrlich-Strasse began, and then walk down the street to the Institutes. This part of Paul Ehrlich-Strasse had still no houses along one side of it, but only building sites, the plots surrounded by fences, with bushes, grass and some trees, including acacias and elder. Ehrlich was always very fond of flowers with bright colours and strong scents, and whenever he saw such a tree, bush or flower in bloom he would pause and breathe in the fragrance, his eye delighting in the colour and form of the blossoms. Then with a slight nod of his head and a little smile he would pass on, saying simply:

'Nice . . . isn't it?'

In the cab rumbling on its way to the Institutes he would often sit silent, deep in thought for quite some time. The expression on his face showed how busily his mind was working. On such occasions I did not venture to disturb him, and did not speak until he himself made some remark which showed what he was thinking about. Generally it was of his worries over Salvarsan and his uneasiness as to what would happen to it and the treatment during the War. Or he would speak of his own illness, impatiently. When I tried to cheer him up, reminding him that the result of years of neglect could not be set right in a moment, that he must be more patient, he only shook his head, stared into space, and muttered, more to himself than to me:

'That will not get better.'

He was often very depressed and discouraged by the War, which he was convinced could not end well, and ought to have been avoided. By the beginning of 1915 he felt that it would be lost. He worried very much about his Salvarsan, because he knew that under war conditions careful treatment would often be impossible, and he feared that the preparation, as made in foreign countries, might be less conscientiously manufactured and cause more unpleasant reactions than usual. This would, of course, reflect discreditably on Salvarsan in general. Also he was deeply distressed by the interruption of his scientific relations with all his foreign friends.

I had to keep on warning him, imploring him not to give way to so many distressing thoughts. When I tried to turn the conversation into less disturbing channels he would agree good-naturedly, saying:

'You are quite right—it is useless to worry.'

Then he would speak affectionately of his grandchildren, who often came to see him. He would even laugh at a funny street-scene we might happen to be passing, or at an odd notice outside a shop.

Sometimes he would talk quite cheerfully about his future scientific plans. Once he said:

'You know, I need never work out anything new at all. If I followed up all the thoughts and problems I have already noted down in "blocks" and put on one side in favour of work on Salvarsan or other more urgent work, if I took up all that again, I could keep a dozen chemical assistants busy with the work for years. Those "blocks" are a real gold mine of discovery!'

This was quite true. There were many ideas which he had never had time to develop. I happened to read quite recently one of his papers written in 1885 and published in the *Charité Annalen*. It was 'On the Character and Treatment of Iodism'. In this paper he reported his experiments with patients who, while undergoing treatment with iodine, suffered from clinical reactions known as iodism, with swelling of the eyelids to such an extent that the eyes could hardly be opened, and violent nasal catarrh. Ehrlich tried treatment with sulphanilic acid and observed that all the symptoms disappeared 'as if by a miracle' within an hour. After twelve days the symptoms reappeared, but on repeating the treatment with sulphanilic acid the same miraculous result was obtained in every case. In spite of the use of very strong doses the patients never had any complications.

That Ehrlich did not at once investigate thoroughly this marvellous action of sulphanilic acid was probably due to the difficult circumstances in which he was living at that time. His chief, Professor von Frerichs, who had given him complete liberty to follow up his own lines of research, had died in that year, and his successor had made the young Dr. Ehrlich devote all his time to the regular duties of a clinical assistant. Then, as we must remember, Ehrlich became infected with tuberculosis and went to Egypt for two years. After his return to Berlin he was occupied with research with Robert Koch on tuberculosis and with Emil von Behring on diphtheria. Then came the work on serum control and serum research at the Steglitz Institute, and after that he became so 'filled up with side-chains' and 'spellbound' by his investigations into arsenical compounds, leading to 606, that he had no time for other fields of work. But I am convinced that if he had only lived a few more years, been able to revive some of his earlier work and develop his many 'block notes', he would almost certainly have repeated his experiments with sulphanilic acid, and it is not fantastic, or even unreasonable, to suppose that he might have been led to try the effect of its amide, sulphanilamide, which had to wait for another two decades before its remarkable chemotherapeutic properties came to light.

In January 1914 he had written to his friend Professor William Welch of Baltimore about an Institute for Vital Staining which he intended to open, with the help of foreign friends, for Professor Goldmann of Freiburg, his best pupil in this line of research.

'It would really be a pity if all these things which I have in my head were to disappear with me, without the "flourish of trumpets and ringing of bells",' he said in this letter to Professor Welch. At the proposed Institute his own ideas about the staining of living cells would have been worked out more extensively. But Professor Goldmann died in 1914, the War broke out, and the plan came to nothing.

In 1915 Ehrlich was more and more often in a depressed frame of mind. His elasticity had never failed when it was a question of mastering even the greatest difficulties; with tenacious perseverance he had always piled experiment upon experiment in order to find a really scientific foundation for his theories. His titanic, heaven-storming optimism had always inspired all his collaborators and pupils; but now he was disheartened. Ehrlich, who had never failed to find the means for the continuation of his experiments, was growing weary. The master of successful scientific argument was discouraged; his failing physical strength and his over-sensitive spirit could no longer withstand what he felt to be the malicious opposition and personal hostility which continued to come from his enemies. He was tired out and too weary to fight any more.

At the beginning of August 1915 he went to Bad Homburg for a holiday and to have treatment and rest in the sanatorium of a friend. But he was only able to enjoy a few days of quiet rest, lovingly cared for by his wife, his daughter Marianne and his grandchildren; for it was there that a second stroke brought his life to a sudden and tragic end. It had been arranged that I should go there now and then, so as to avoid a too great accumulation of work during his holiday. I was asked by Frau Ehrlich to go on a certain day, and when I arrived I was told the terrible news. He had had the stroke during the previous night, and was sinking rapidly. He still recognised me, and was able to exchange a few kind words with me, but I could not tell him the news that I had moved into Frankfurt from the little Taunus village where I had lived for some years, so that I should be more easily at his disposal. I had been longing to tell him this as I knew it would please him. It was a great grief to me that I was not able to do so, for by then the news was of no value.

Ehrlich's elder daughter Steffa and his two sons-in-law hurried to him when summoned by telegram. His wife, the true and faithful companion of his life, and all his family were with him when he drew his last breath and his eyes closed forever. It was 20 August, 1915.

Here again, as in my small book 'Paul Ehrlich als Mensch und Arbeiter'[1] ('Paul Ehrlich, the man and his work'), I should like to quote the following passage from Professor Arnold Berliner's obituary notice:[2]

'At the dawn of history, so Goethe tells us, men held a solemn and sometimes terrifying belief. They imagined their ancestors seated in silent communion in great caves in a circle of thrones. When a new soul entered this company, they would stand and bow to welcome him, if he was worthy enough. The ancestors are the great men whose services to humanity are recorded in the Book of Eternity. We can be sure that they will bow deeply in profound veneration to the man now entering their presence.'

We who survived him will always remember Ehrlich's great genius and wonderful character with the most profound feeling of thankfulness for his life.

He was buried in the Jewish Cemetery of Frankfurt. On top of the two high columns at the entrance to the box-edged tomb were, visible from afar, the Star of David and the Snake of

[1] *Loc. cit.*
[2] *Naturwissenschaften*, No. 36, 3 September, 1915.

Ehrlich's tomb. The lower picture shows the inscription

Aesculapius. The tomb was covered with a large slab of marble from the quarries of his native Silesia. Engraved upon it were only his name and the dates of the beginning and end of his remarkable life. At the head of the tomb, on a high stone carved from a natural block of marble was a large vase of porphyritic rock containing trailing rose bushes with an abundance of blossoms. So his resting place was covered with the falling petals of these glowing flowers.

     .   .   .   .   .

The gap which his premature death made can never be filled. In conditions far more terrible than at that time more than thirty years ago, the world has now been devastated by the tumult and stress of six years of another war. Only the shining examples of great men can save us from discouragement and faintheartedness in the face of the inhuman atrocities and destruction which have surrounded us—only the example of a man like Ehrlich, a man who dedicated and sacrificed his whole life to the welfare and healing of mankind, never failing in his idealism, his optimism and his faith, until he finally broke down from exhaustion. To Ehrlich nothing on earth mattered except scientific research aimed at overcoming suffering and disease, and increasing the happiness of mankind. His unshakable and unwavering faith in the progress of his work was like a warming flame which filled his whole nature and shone forth in all his actions.

On 20 August, 1915, *The Times* published an obituary notice of him in which, transcending the animosities of war, it said:

    'The vast number of problems he set himself bear witness to the strength of his imagination. He opened "new doors to the unknown" and the whole world at this hour is his debtor.'

PERSONAL DATES

1854   14 March, born in Strehlen (Upper Silesia). Attended elementary school in this town. College in Breslau. Studied Medicine at the Universities of Breslau, Strassburg, Freiburg and Leipzig.

1878   Degree Thesis and graduation as M.D. at the University of Leipzig. In the same year Assistant of Professor von Frerichs, Director of the Charité Hospital, Medical Clinic, Berlin. Remained until 1887 as Senior Physician.

1884   Grade of Professor given to him.

1887   Became Lecturer. During his experimental investigations and clinical work on tuberculosis, Ehrlich acquired a tuberculous infection on account of which he had to interrupt his activity. Went to Egypt for two years, where he completely recovered from his infection.

1889   Back in Berlin. Established a small research laboratory of his own, but not having there such ample facilities as he required he accepted an invitation from Robert Koch to work at his newly created Institute

1890   for Infectious Diseases at Berlin. His studies in immunity at this Institute were of great importance to Emil von Behring's discovery of diphtheria antitoxin. Worked out this treatment so completely and finally that reliable methods for therapy were introduced into the human treatment of diphtheria infections which have remained the standard ever since for the entire medical world. Was also made Extraordinary Professor at the University of Berlin.

    The Director in the Prussian Ministry for Educational and Medical Affairs, Dr. Althoff, having recognised at an early date the importance of Ehrlich's research work, suggested to the Prussian Government the foundation of a State Institute for Serum Research and Serum Control.

1896   This Institute was opened in the small suburban town of Berlin, Steglitz, with Paul Ehrlich as Director. Here he started a laboratory of his own to carry on his investigations. Soon after this, however, Dr. Althoff, in collaboration with the Lord Mayor of Frankfurt a.M., Dr. Adickes, succeeded in finding more favourable surroundings for Ehrlich's work. A greater Institute for Experimental Therapy was built in Frankfurt.

1898   The State Institute for Serum Research and Serum Control at Steglitz was transferred to this Institute, with widely extended scientific powers, under the Directorship of Paul Ehrlich.

    A few years later, Mrs. Franzisca Speyer, of the Frankfurt family Speyer-Ellissen, who was greatly interested in the work of Ehrlich, offered to make a very large donation in order to build a research institute exclusively for Ehrlich's studies in Chemotherapy. This being Ehrlich's favourite field of investigation, the ideas of which dated back to the early years of his university studies, he gladly accepted the offer. The new 'Georg Speyer-Haus' for Chemotherapeutical Research—so called by Frau Speyer in memory of her deceased husband —was therefore built next to the State Institute for Experimental Therapy.

1906   The 'Georg Speyer-House' was taken over by Ehrlich as Director. Ample means to carry on his research work were now placed at his disposal. Two big Institutes were entrusted to his care and were carried on with a success which was world wide.

1897   Ehrlich was elected Privy Medical Counsel by the Government.
1907   He was promoted to a higher rank of this Counsel.
1908   Together with Professor Metchnikoff of the Institut Pasteur in Paris, he received the *Nobel Prize for Medicine* for successful work in the fields of research in immunity.
1911   He received the highest rank: Real Privy Counsel with the title of Excellency.
1912   The former Sandhofstrasse with the two Research Institutes of Ehrlich was called 'Paul Ehrlich-Strasse' in his honour, and the City of Frankfurt conferred on him the Freedom of the City.
20 August, 1915   Paul Ehrlich died, at the age of sixty-one. His tomb is in the Jewish Cemetery in Frankfurt a.M.

DOCTORATES

1904	Chicago	LL.D.
1905	Göttingen	Prof. honor.
1907	Oxford	D.C.L.
1911	Athens	Dr.phil.h.c.
1912	Breslau	Dr.med.h.c.

PRIZES OF HONOUR

1887   Senckenberg Naturforschende Gesellschaft, Frankfurt a.M. *Tiedemann Prize* for Ehrlich's publication: 'Das Sauerstoffbedürfnis des Organismus' ('The Need of Oxygen of the Organism').
1906   *Prize of Honour* at the XVth International Congress of Medicine at Lisbon.
1908   *Nobel Prize* for Medicine (together with Professor Metchnikoff of the Institut Pasteur, Paris), for their studies in immunity.
1911   Society of German Chemists, *Liebig Medaille*.
1914   Cameron Prize of Edinburgh.

ORDERS GIVEN TO PAUL EHRLICH

Prussia
 Order of the Crown, Second Degree.
 Order of the Red Eagle, Second Degree.
Palatinate
 Cavalier Cross of the order of Berthold I of Zähringen.
Denmark
 Commander Cross of the Danebrog Order, Second Degree.
Norway
 Commander Cross of the Royal Norvegian St. Olaf Order, Second Degree.
Spain
 Great Cross of the Order of Alfonso XII, with Star and Cross.
Serbia
 Great Cross of the Order of St. Sava.
Bavaria
 Member of the Bavarian Maximilian Order.
Russia
 Order of St. Anne, First Degree, with Diamonds, Star and Cross.
Venezuela
 Order of the Bust of Bolivar, Second Degree, with Precious Stones.
Japan
 Order of the Rising Sun, Third Degree.
Roumania
 Cross for Sanitary Merits, First Degree.

MEMBERSHIP OF SCIENTIFIC SOCIETIES

1887	10 May	Senckenbergische Naturforschende Gesellschaft, Frankfurt a.M.	Corresponding Member
1899	Dec.	Senckenbergische Naturforschende Gesellschaft, Frankfurt a.M.	Ordinary Member.
1900		Balneological Society, Berlin.	Honorary Member.
1900	7 April	Royal Danish Society of Sciences, Copenhagen.	Foreign Member.
1902		International Society for Combat against Tuberculosis, Berlin.	Honorary Member.
1902	13 Feb.	German Chemical Society, Berlin.	Member of the Committee.
1903		Silesian Society for Home Culture	Corresponding Member.
1903		Royal Academy of Medicine, Turin.	,, ,,
1904	Jan.	Royal Academy of Sciences, Bologna.	,, ,,
1904	27 Jan.	Society for Internal Medicine Vienna.	Honorary Member.
1904	18 March	Imperial and Royal Society of Physicians, Vienna.	,, ,,
1904	2 April	The New York Academy of Medicine.	,, ,,
1904	Oct.	Royal Society of Sciences, Göttingen.	Foreign Member of the mathematical and physical class.
1904	Dec.	Royal Society of Medicine and Natural Science, Brussels.	Corresponding Member.
1904		Academy of Sciences, Washington.	Foreign Member.

1904		Societas therapeutica Mosquana, Moscow	Honorary Member.
1905	23 May	Academie de Médécine, Paris.	Foreign Member.
1905	9 Dec.	Societas Regia Medicorum (Medical Society), Budapest.	Honorary Member.
1906	Feb.	Medical Society of Finland, Helsingfors.	,, ,,
1906	10 Oct.	Society of Physicians, Munich.	,, ,,
1906	22 Dec.	Société de Biologie, Paris.	Ordinary Member.
1907	10 June	Pathological Society of Great Britain and Ireland.	Honorary Member.
1907		Society of Tropical Medicine and Hygiene, London.	,, ,,
1907	12 July	R. Academia dei Lincei, Rome.	Foreign Member.
1907	13 July	Royal Institute of Public Health, London.	Honorary Member.
1907	18 Dec.	Medical Society of Berlin.	,, ,,
1908	14 Feb.	Société de Pathologie Exotique (Institut Pasteur), Paris.	,, ,,
1908	27 June	Physical-Medical Society, Erlangen.	,, ,,
1908	10 Oct.	Society for the Knowledge of Nature and Medical Treatment, Dresden.	,, ,,
1908	25 Oct.	Swedish Medical Society, Stockholm.	,, ,,
1908	14 Dec.	Physical Society, Frankfurt a.M.	,, ,
1909	Feb.	Medical Society, St. Petersburg.	,, ,,
1910	28 Jan.	Microbiological Society, St. Petersburg.	,, ,,
.1910	20 May	Royal Academy of Medicine, Turin.	,, ,,
1910	June	Royal Society, London.	,, ,,
1910	7 Sept.	Société Médicale Impériale du Caucase.	,, ,,
1910	3 Oct.	International Commission for the Study of the Causes of Mental Diseases and their Prophylaxis, Berlin.	,, ,,
1910		Royal Swedish Academy of Sciences, Stockholm.	Foreign Member.
1910	6 Oct.	German Society of Tropical Medicine, Hamburg.	Honorary Member.
1910	7 Nov.	Society of Physicians, Odessa.	,, ,,
1910	7 Nov.	Société Khédiviale de Médécine, Cairo.	,, ,,
1910	20 Nov.	Commission Internationale pour l'étude des causes des maladies mentales et leur prophylaxie, Rome.	,, ,,
1910	25 Nov	Medical Society of Jekaterinoslaw.	,, ,,
1910	14 Dec.	Vienna Dermatological Society.	,, ,,
1910	21 Dec.	Medical Society of Serbia, Belgrade.	,, ,,
1910	27 Dec.	Physico-Medical Society, Saratow.	,, ,,
1911	1 Feb.	Union of the St. Petersburg Physicians for Children.	,, ,,
1911	18 Feb.	Société Impériale de Médécine, Constantinople.	,, ,,
1911		K. Vetenskaps Societeten, Upsala (Royal Society of Sciences).	Ordinary Member.
1911	16 June	Academia Romana, Bucarest.	Honorary Member.
1911	17 Nov.	Union of Physicians, Smolensk.	,, ,,
1911	27 Nov.	Vereenigung voor Mikrobiologie, Delft, Holland.	Corresponding Member.
1911	19 Dec.	Royal Medical Society, Edinburgh.	Honorary Member.
1911	30 Dec.	Academie Royal de Médécine, Brussels.	,, ,,

1911		Imperial Institute for Experimental Therapy, St. Petersburg.	Honorary Member.
1912		Physiological Society of London.	,, ,,
1912		Society of Internal Medicine, Berlin.	,, ,,
1912	3 April	Society of Cancer Research of the Palatinate, Heidelberg.	,, ,,
1912	28 March	Charkow Veterinary Institute.	,, ,,
1912	5 Aug.	Sociedade Brazileira de Dermatologia.	Honorary President.
1912	18 April	Academia Nacional de Caracas.	Corresponding Member.
1912	18 May	Freedom of the City of Strehlen (Silesia).	
1912	6 Nov.	Société Royale des Sciences médicales et naturelles, Brussels.	Honorary Member.
1912	Nov.	German Society of Tradesmen for Recreation-Homes.	Member of Committee.
1912		Dermatological Society, Odessa.	Honorary Member.
1912	Dec.	Sömmering-Prize Commission.	Member.
1912	Dec.	Medical Society of Athens.	Honorary Member.
1913	11 Feb.	Society for Natural Sciences, Braunschweig.	,, ,,
1913	28 April	German Chemical Society, Berlin.	,, ,,
1913	25 July	Union of Physicians, Archangelsk.	,, ,,
1913	July	Society of Physicians, Odessa.	,, ,,
1913		Society of German Physicians for Mental Diseases, Berlin.	,, ,,
1913	Oct.	Medical Society of Orel.	,, ,,
1913	Oct.	Society of Veterinary Doctors of the Veterinary Institute of Kasan.	,, ,,
1913		Harveian Society of London.	Foreign Member.
1913	30 Dec.	Société de Biologie, Paris.	Honorary Member.
1913	10 Dec.	Societa Italiana di Dermatologia e Sifiligrafia, Rome.	,, ,,
1914	4 March	Societa Medico-chirurgica di Bologna.	Corresponding Member.
1914	19 March	Society of Specialists for Children, Moscow.	Honorary Member.
1914	April	Norwegisk Videnskaps Selskapet, Section of Natural Science, Christiana.	Foreign Member.
1914	4 March	Society of Jewish Physicians of the Ottoman State, Constantinople.	Honorary Member.
1915	July	Pharmaceutical Society, Berlin.	,, ,,